BENET'S

ARTEFACTS OF ENGLAND
& THE UNITED KINGDOM
CURRENT VALUES

Roman Edition 2016

Published by Greenlight Publishing

Written and Compiled by Brett Hammond

BENET'S ARTEFACTS
OF ENGLAND & THE UNITED KINGDOM
CURRENT VALUES
ROMAN EDITION

Written and Compiled by:
Brett Hammond, CEO, TimeLine Auctions,
TimeLine Auctions Limited,
The Court House, 363 Main Road, Harwich,
Essex CO12 4DN, UK
Tel.: +44 (0) 1277 815121
Email: enquiries@timelineauctions.com
www.timelineauctions.com

Published by:
Greenlight Publishing, The Publishing House,
119 Newland Street, Witham, Essex CM8 1WF
Tel: 01376 521900
www.greenlightpublishing.co.uk

Origination by Christine Jennett

Cover by Damir Radić

ISBN 9781897738610

INTRODUCTION TO THE ROMAN EDITION

Welcome to the Roman edition of *Benet's Artefacts*, a handy visual guide to Roman period objects found in the United Kingdom and Europe.

This volume follows the format of the previous work, *Benet's Medieval Artefacts*. Each section includes a sample of the various classes of Roman object most commonly encountered, which provides a handy reference guide to types for the period as a whole. No attempt has been made to include every known form and variant of finger ring or plate brooch, but all the major types of each are represented in these pages.

As with previous editions of *Benet's*, each entry is illustrated with a good, clear colour photograph, as well as a short description and the overall size in millimetres. Each entry also features a suggested price-range for the item, but it must be borne in mind that prices are affected by the object's condition and rarity on the one hand, and the number of collectors seeking the item on the other hand. For these reasons a complete revision of previously published prices has been undertaken.

Due to the distinctive nature of the culture, identification of Roman items is less contentious than for some other types of material, but scope still exists for doubt and error.

Accurate information regarding findspot can help to market any artefact. Objects recorded with the Finds Liaison Officers of the Portable Antiquities Scheme are studied by professionals, often with years of experience and access to large reference libraries. The greater the number of items recorded with the scheme, the better the coverage of its records and thus the more useful it becomes as a reference tool. Items which at first appear rare or unusual may in time prove to be commonplace.

As would be expected for Roman material, there are many items with religious ornament and iconography in these pages. Votive items and figurines can often be attributed to a particular deity, such as Minerva or Hercules, which increases their interest for collectors and prospective purchasers. Likewise some military equipment can be assigned to a particular legion if it bears an appropriate stamped mark.

Thank you for choosing *Benet's Roman Artefacts*. We hope you will find it useful and enjoyable.

ACKNOWLEDGEMENTS

Benet's Roman is the latest title in the series of *Benet's* books that have become a standard form of reference.

It is as always a team effort in which the skills and knowledge of many individuals have been pooled in compiling the text and images.

Special thanks are due to several of the leading specialists at TimeLine Auctions for their assistance with this project; namely Stephen Pollington, Michaela Šimonová and Michael Healy.

VALUES

The price ranges indicated in this book represent what a collector or museum might be prepared to pay, not what a dealer might offer.

The prices refer to the illustrated objects in the condition shown. If you have an artefact in better or worse condition, the price should be adjusted accordingly. The valuations are based on four criteria:

1. Condition

2. Quality of Workmanship

3. Rarity

4. Demand

Generally, all other factors being equal, it is quality in design and execution which commands a premium. The highest standards of workmanship are rare and exceptional in any age: objects which display these qualities are always the most prized.

CONTENTS

ROMAN BRITAIN

Britain's first known contact with Rome took place in 55 BC when Julius Caesar led a small expeditionary force across the Channel from Gaul, in order to intervene in a local political dispute and to disrupt British assistance to the Gallic tribes resisting Roman invasion. The first campaign established a Roman bridgehead in Kent, and the following year (54 BC) a pro-Roman leader, Mandubracius, was installed as king of the Trinovantes in what is now southeast England.

The next direct contact with Roman power came in 43 AD when the Emperor Claudius launched a full-scale invasion through Kent. Conquest of the southern and eastern areas of Britain proceeded quickly and later extended to the west, but the north of Britain always proved problematic, lacking the economic resources to make its military conquest profitable for the Empire.

Roman tactics switched from sensitive diplomacy to severe arrogance within a generation. The revolt of Boudicca in 61 AD temporarily halted Roman plans for the settlement of large numbers of retired soldiers in the province. The brutal treatment of Roman citizens in Colchester, London and St. Albans by Boudicca's forces mirrored the treatment she and her daughters underwent at the hands of the Roman military. At the same time, the unifying power of the British priesthood of druids was crushed and the great religious sanctuary on Anglesey was destroyed.

The Roman way of life came to be emulated by wealthy landowners in the south and east; the economy of production based on the *villa* estate was widely adopted by the end of the 1st century AD.

Client kings were established initially to rule existing tribal populations until the 2nd century AD when the *Provincia Britannia* was established as a fully-administered part of the Empire. A turf and wooden frontier – the Antonine Wall – was established as the empire's northern border in about 142 AD, but this boundary and its territory was eventually surrendered around 155 AD to be replaced by the stone-built Hadrian's Wall to the south, begun around 120 AD. Britain was effectively organised into a northern military zone ruled from *Eboracum* (York) and a southern civil zone from *Londinium* (London). The old administrative capital of *Camulodunum* (Colchester) was destroyed by Boudicca's troops and never regained its former importance.

Septimius Severus led an army into *Caledonia* (Scotland) in about 208 AD with a view to annexing the territory, but the weather and terrain in combination with the guerrilla tactics of the locals made decisive battle impossible and the frontier remained unchanged. The later years of the 3rd century saw a series of rebellions and secessions on the continent; Britain was often only marginal in these but was affected by the part played by Gaul (e.g. the so-called Gallic Empire under Postumus, 259-274 AD).

Fragmentation of the Empire in the 4th century alongside religious and economic changes and re-organization of the administration left Britain exposed to decline. Usurpers such as Magnus Maximus (rebelled 383, died 388) raised military units which took part in abortive campaigns on the continent and depleted the ability of *Britannia* to resist attacks from Ireland and across the North Sea.

Roman domination of Britain lasted until the early years of the 5th century although the ties to the Empire had been loosened from the mid-4th century onwards following a series of depopulations through plague, civil insurrections, rebellions and sponsorship of usurpers. *Britannia* required a military force of at least three legions to maintain Roman rule, which formed a sufficient powerbase for any motivated governor with ambitions of creating a separate political unit in Britain divorced from the Empire itself. A series of abortive attempts at secession made the island troublesome and expensive to administer. Raiding of the exposed coast by sailors from the North Sea rim prompted the creation of a dedicated patrol fleet in the Channel, the *Classis Britannica* (British fleet), and the establishment of the 'Saxon Shore' (*Litus Saxonicum*) as a militarised border zone in the south and east.

By the 4th century, Britain was re-organised into four provinces named *Britannia I*, *Britannia II*, *Maxima Caesariensis*, and *Flavia Caesariensis*, while the existence and extent of a fifth named Valentia is disputed. These smaller units were less easy to form into a single powerbase. Yet Constantine I (272-337) launched his successful bid for the imperial throne from York in 306 AD.

Ultimately, direct rule of the British provinces from Rome ended and a century of turmoil followed. Bronze coin production apparently ceased in the third quarter of the 4th century. The fate of the Roman military in Britain is mostly unknown, but some legions were withdrawn to the continent to assist with the protection of the Empire. Landowners and urban authorities may have organised their own defence, using some of the many prisoners of war generated by large-scale warfare on the continent.

The effect of the Roman presence in Britain can be seen in the quantities of coins and small bronze objects which were then in use and are still commonly found today. Many of these objects are of standard types which may be found from modern Syria to Portugal, while others are more restricted in distribution, especially to the frontier provinces. The major economic and military links of Britain appear to have been with Gaul and *Germania*.

Roman innovations found in the material record include locks, keys, glassware, cosmetic and surgical instruments, some types of cooking equipment, storage vessels and tableware, writing materials and dress items such as buckles and *phalerae*. Some access to literacy even at the end of the Roman period is shown by the many short inscriptions on jewellery, military equipment and elsewhere.

RINGS & OTHER JEWELLERY

Finger rings were made in quantity in the Roman period, and they formed a recognisable badge of status and authority. Gold, silver, bone and bronze were popular materials from which to fashion them. Some rings featured the shank and bits of a key to one edge.

A plain bronze hoop with small raised bezel must have been within the means of all but the poorest members of society. More elaborate forms with sloping, flattened or scrolled shoulders developed, as well as the clasped-hands and other symbolic types. Typological studies have established the sequence of development, so that most rings can be dated quite closely.

The bezel might be set with a gemstone or glass jewel, either flat or a rounded cabochon type. Such flat stones were often carved with an image or with a short text, called an intaglio; this is much rarer on cabochon stones.

Other jewellery items included torcs and neck-rings, chain necklaces, earrings, bracelets and armrings, diadems, hairpins and combs, and various types of pendant. Glass, shell, nicolo and cameo inserts were used to enliven plain surfaces as well as punched and freehand carved detailing.

Roman ladies went to great lengths to keep up with the fashions in dress and hairstyles set by the imperial court, many of which can be tracked through the profile bust images on Roman coins. Cosmetics of various kinds formed an important part of the public image of the wealthy.

RN-60472
Gold Ring
with Wolf
and Twins
21mm
£800-£1,000

RN-51486
Gold
Legionary
Ring
21mm
'LEGIIIIFF' for
Legio IIII Flavia
Felix
£800-£1,000

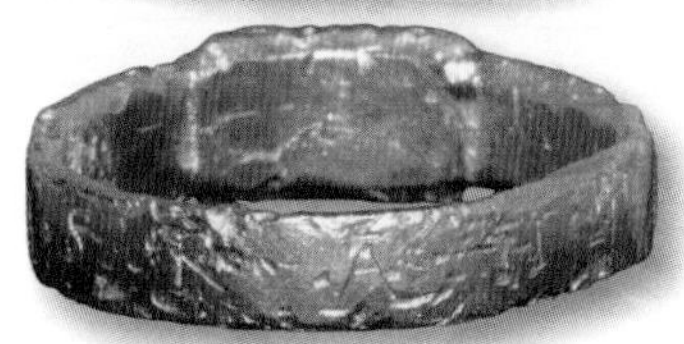

RN-37484
Gold Ring
26mm
Inscribed 'CONSTANTINO' and
'FIDEM' (loyal to Constantine)
From £500

RN-57647
Gold Ring with Fortuna
23mm
£600-£800

RN-45982
Gold Ring with Justitia
30mm
£500-£700

RN-69449
Gold Marriage Ring with Clasped Hands
20mm
£400-£600

RN-56452
Gold Marriage Ring
23mm
With busts of the couple
£400-£600

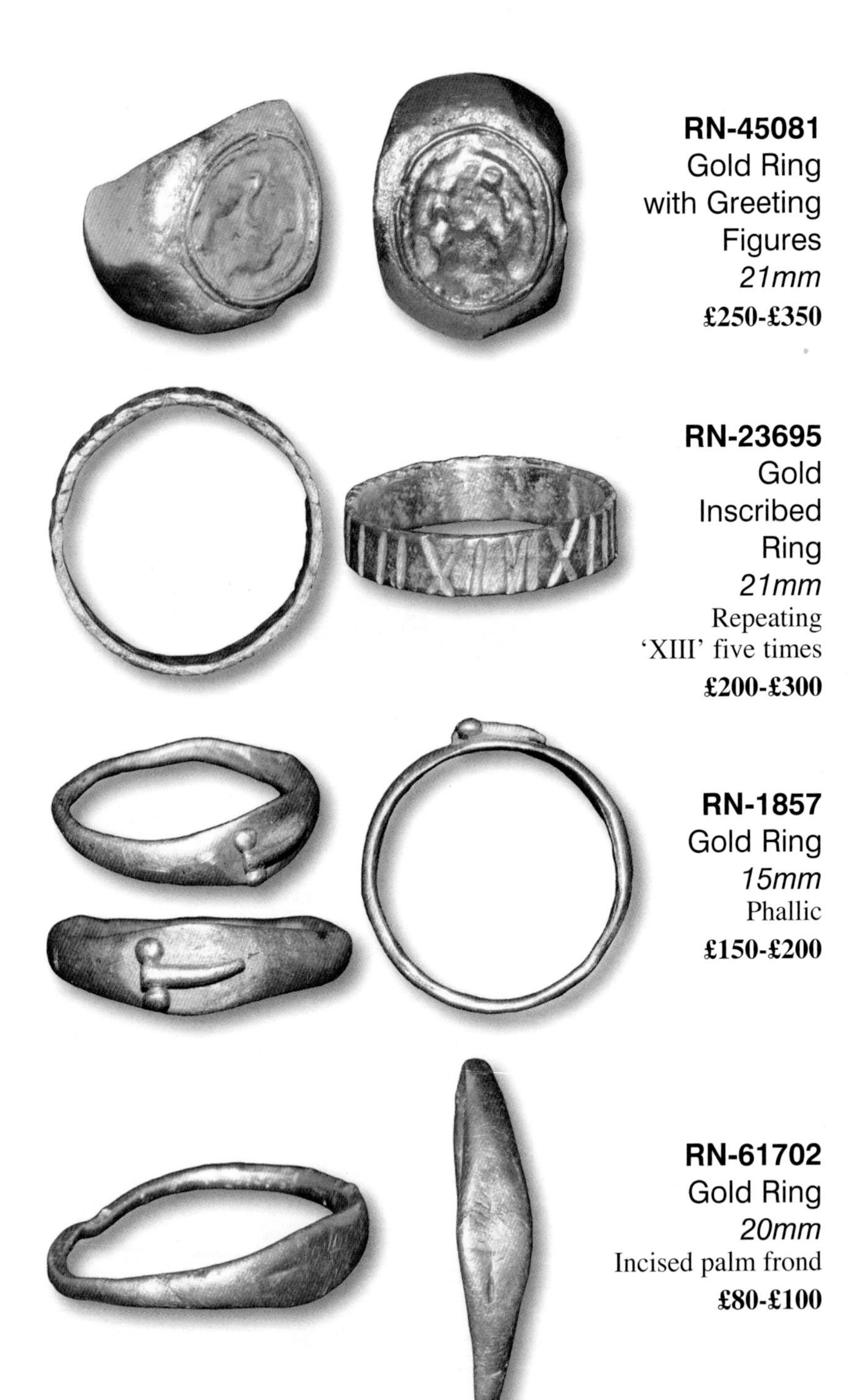

RN-45081
Gold Ring
with Greeting
Figures
21mm
£250-£350

RN-23695
Gold
Inscribed
Ring
21mm
Repeating
'XIII' five times
£200-£300

RN-1857
Gold Ring
15mm
Phallic
£150-£200

RN-61702
Gold Ring
20mm
Incised palm frond
£80-£100

RN-57917
Gold Ring with Intaglio of an Empress
26mm
From £3,000

RN-62475
Gold Ring with Emperor Intaglio
25mm
From £3,000

RN-57372
Gold Ring with Male Bust Intaglio
29mm
From £1,000

RN-53049
Gold Ring with Goddess Intaglio
22mm
£250-£350

RN-63790
Gold Ring with Playing Cupids Intaglio
23mm
Greek legend to the outer edge 'E? / TY / XHO / C'
From £2,000

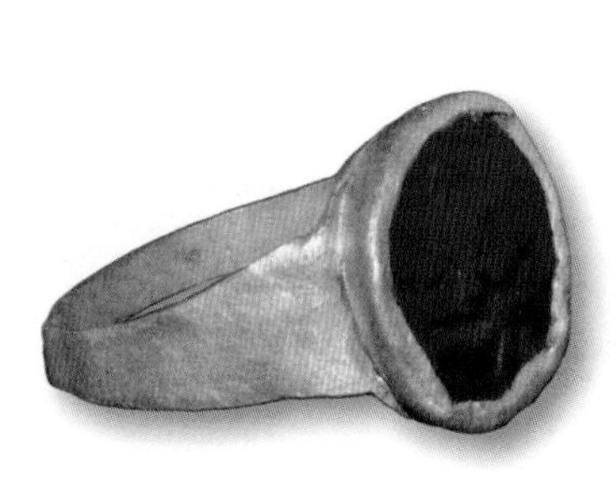

RN-45785
Gold and Carnelian Ring
18mm
Cupid and Psyche intaglio
£200-£300

RN-45877
Gold Ring with Minerva Intaglio
27mm
From £1,000

RN-21090
Gold Ring with Minerva Intaglio
27mm
£500-£700

RN-60729
Gold Ring with Minerva Intaglio
21mm
£300-£400

RN-54701
Gold Ring with Mercury Intaglio
19mm
£400-£600

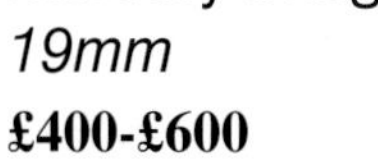

RN-52331
Gold Ring with Mercury Intaglio
28mm
£400-£600

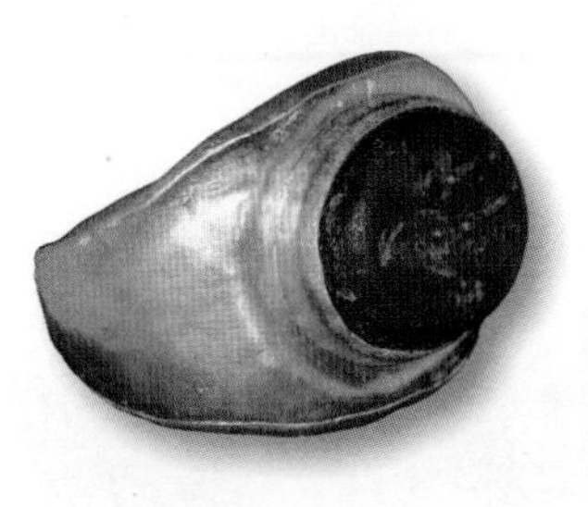

RN-45854
Gold Ring with Mercury Intaglio
22mm
£400-£600

RN-35841
Gold Ring with
Mercury Intaglio
21mm
£400-£600

RN-48706
Gold Ring with
Mercury Intaglio
19mm
£250-£350

RN-16223
Gold
Ring with
Minerva
Intaglio
20mm
£300-£400

RN-33519
Ring with
Victory
Intaglio
18mm
£300-£400

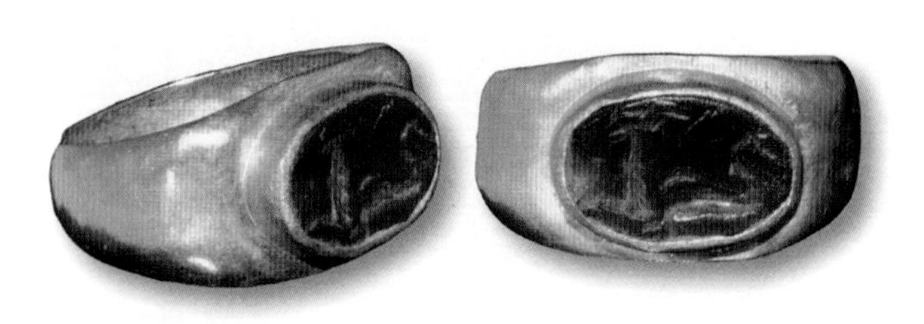

RN-61428
Gold Ring with Winged Victory Intaglio
24mm
£250-£350

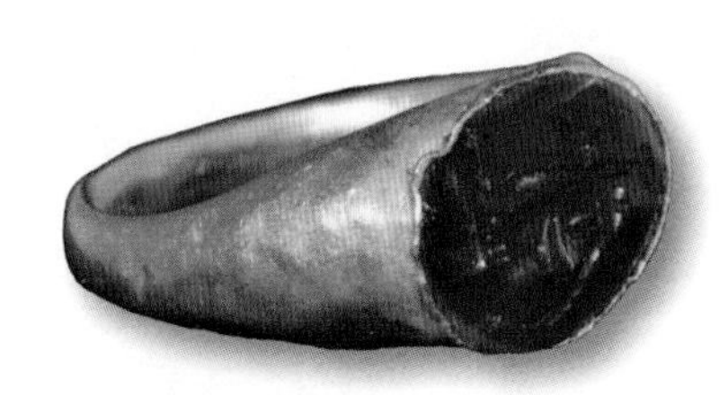

RN-50572
Gold Ring with Fortuna Intaglio
19mm
£300-£400

RN-33518
Gold Ring with Fortuna Intaglio
19mm
£300-£400

RN-62478
Gold Ring with Diana Intaglio
28mm
From £2,000

RN-57916
Gold Ring with Pan and Cockerel Intaglio
27mm
From £1,500

RN-39095
Gold Ring with Carnelian Apollo Intaglio
21mm
From £1,500

RN-45880
Gold Ring with Tyche Intaglio
31mm
From £1,000

RN-57915
Gold Ring with Standing Harpocrates Intaglio
26mm
From £1,000

RN-47327
Gold Ring with
Abundantia Intaglio
28mm
£800-£1,000

RN-60820
Gold Ring with
Jupiter Intaglio
23mm
£500-£700

RN-35764
Gold Ring with
Kneeling Mars
Intaglio
18mm
£300-£400

RN-53881
Gold Ring with
Hercules Bust
Intaglio
23mm
£300-£400

RN-23473
Gold Intaglio Ring with Standing Figure
19mm
£300-£400

RN-69565
Eagle Intaglio Inscribed to the Reverse in Modern Gold Ring
20mm
£500-£700

RN-30461
Gold Ring
19mm
Imperial eagle perched between two legionary standards
From £800

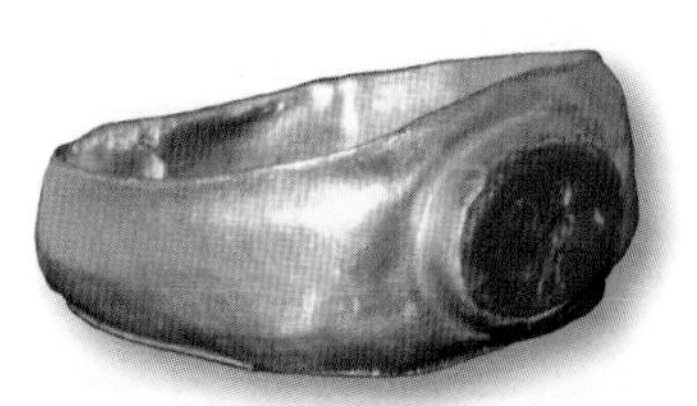

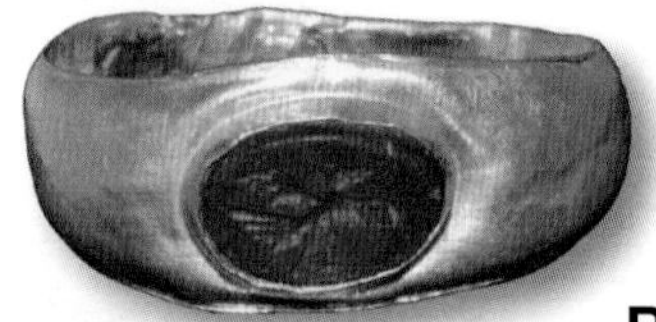

RN-35845
Gold Ring with Eagle Intaglio
21mm
£300-£400

RN-17754
Gold Finger Ring with
Two Birds Intaglio
20mm
£300-£400

RN-39094
Gold Ring with Lion and Horse Intaglio
24mm
From £1,000

RN-51360
Gold Ring with
Lion Intaglio
21mm
£250-£350

RN-16224
Gold Ring with Capricorn Intaglio
21mm
£300-£400

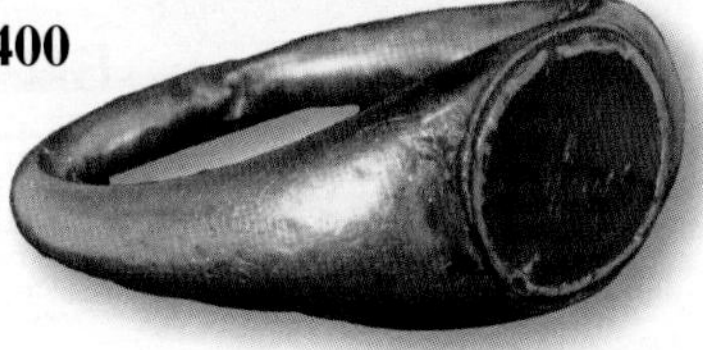

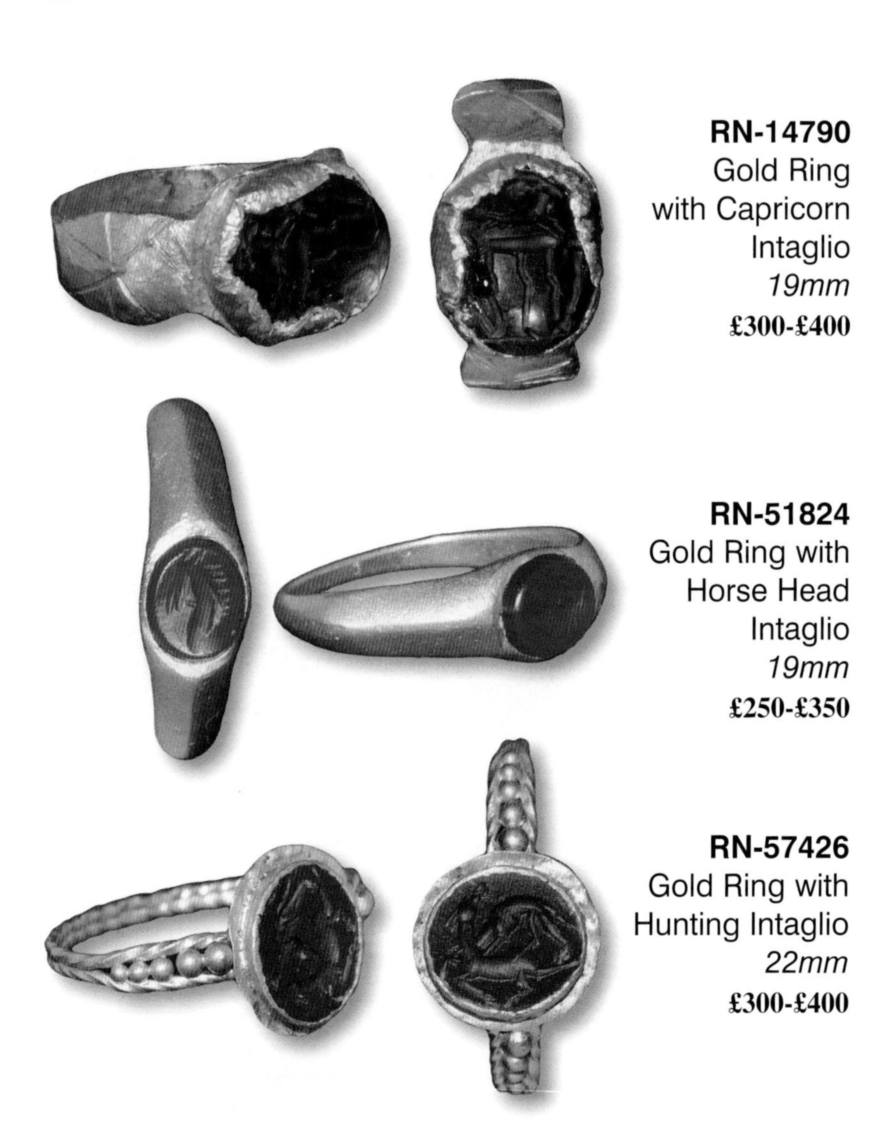

RN-14790
Gold Ring
with Capricorn
Intaglio
19mm
£300-£400

RN-51824
Gold Ring with
Horse Head
Intaglio
19mm
£250-£350

RN-57426
Gold Ring with
Hunting Intaglio
22mm
£300-£400

RN-9850
Gold Ring with Birds Intaglio
23mm
£200-£300

RN-2536
Gold Sacred Fire
Intaglio Ring
23mm
£400-£600

RN-64998
Gold Ring
29mm
Inscribed 'VET / XI * CL / LEG' for a veteran of Legio XI Claudia
From £2,000

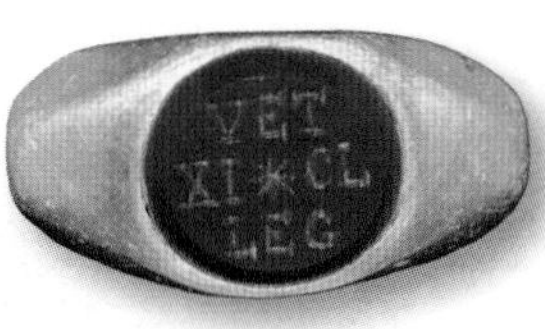

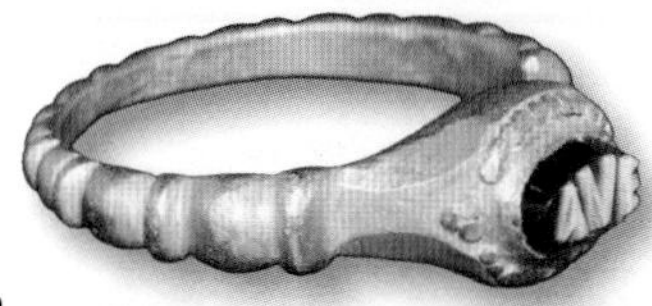

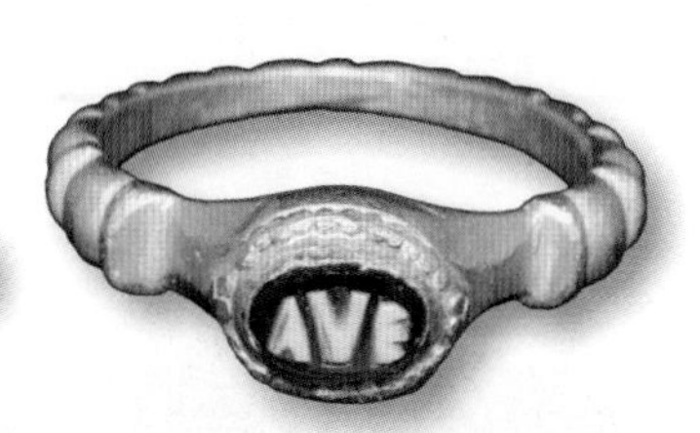

RN-67778
Gold Ring with 'Greetings' Cameo
22mm
£800-£1,000

RN-35763
Gold Ring with Cameo
19mm
Reserved 'BENE' ([be] well) text
£250-£350

RN-34353
Gold Ring
22mm
'SPQR' legend
'Senatus Populusque Romanus' ('Senate and People of Rome')
£600-£800

RN-9854
Gold Ring
25mm
Inscribed 'IXA'
£250-£350

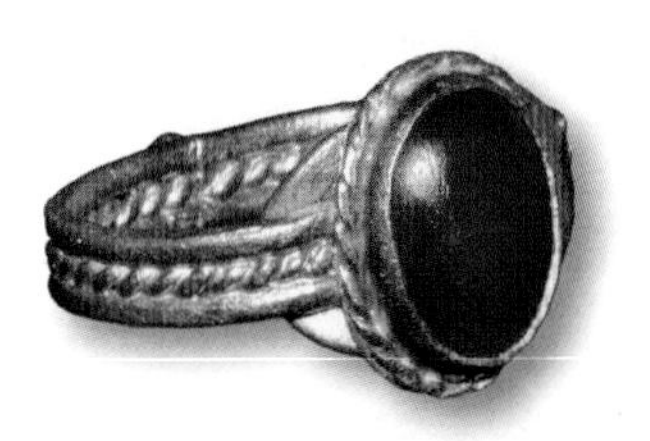

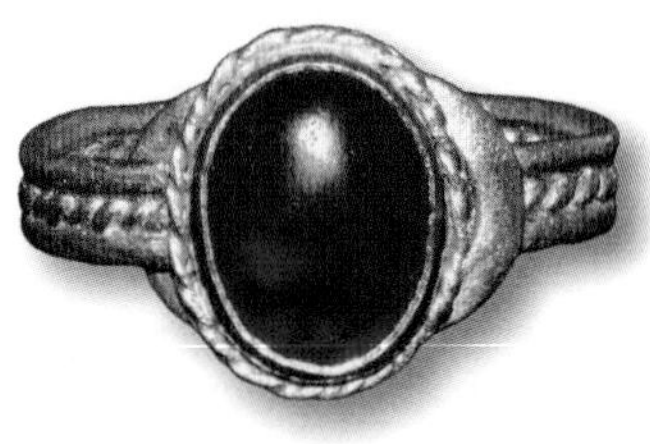

RN-17955
Gold Ring
21mm
Gordian knot and red glass bezel
£800-£1,000

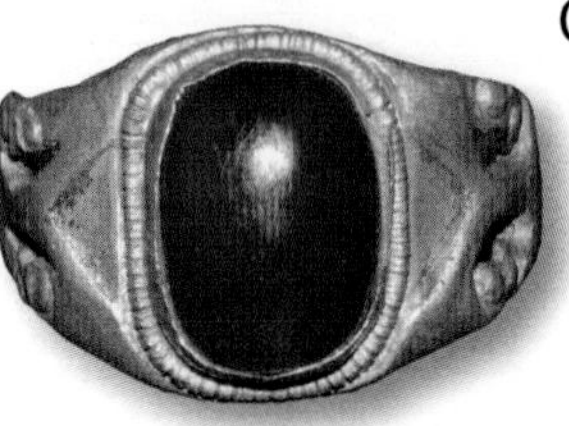

RN-19276
Gold Openwork Ring
25mm
With carnelian cabochon
From £800

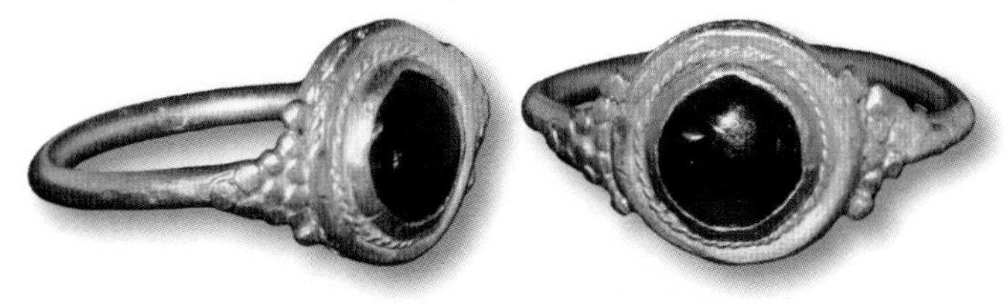

RN-51828
Gold Ring
22mm
With garnet cabochon
£300-£400

RN-11613
Gold Ring
18mm
Carnelian cabochon
£300-£400

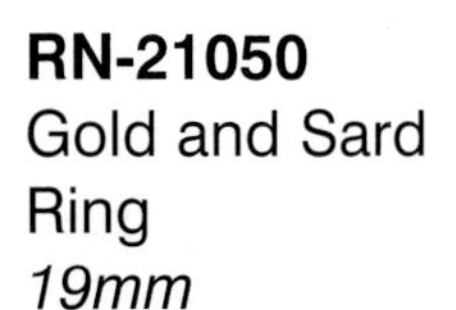

RN-21050
Gold and Sard Ring
19mm
£200-£300

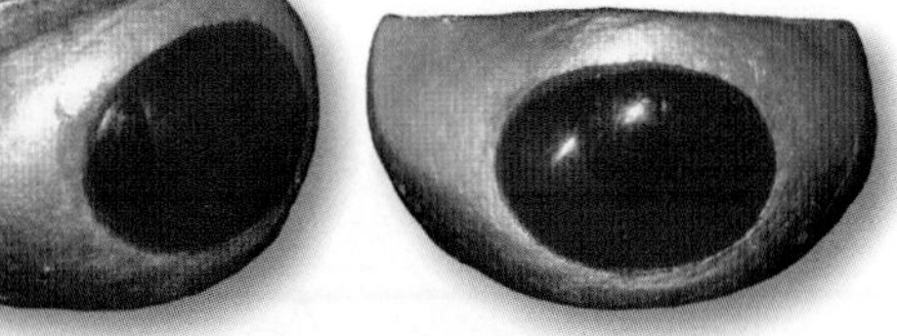

RN-58912
Gold Ring
22mm
With garnets and blue glass
£300-£400

RN-56153
Gold Ring
18mm
With amethyst cabochon
£200-£300

RN-56114
Gold Ring with Anchor and Dolphins
24mm
From £3,000

RN-61314
Gold Ring with Nicolo Female Figure
26mm
From £1,500

RN-37483
Gold Ring with Mercury Intaglio
18mm
From £1,000

RN-50517
Gold
Ring with
Theseus
Intaglio
21mm
From £800

RN-23366
Gold Intaglio
Ring with
Standing
Figure
22mm
£400-£600

RN-61648
Gold Ring with
Cameo of an
Empress
26mm
From £1,000

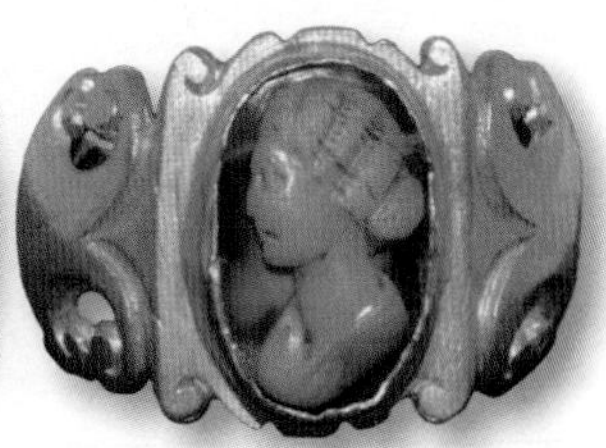

RN-16341
Gold Ring
with Empress
Cameo
21mm
£600-£800

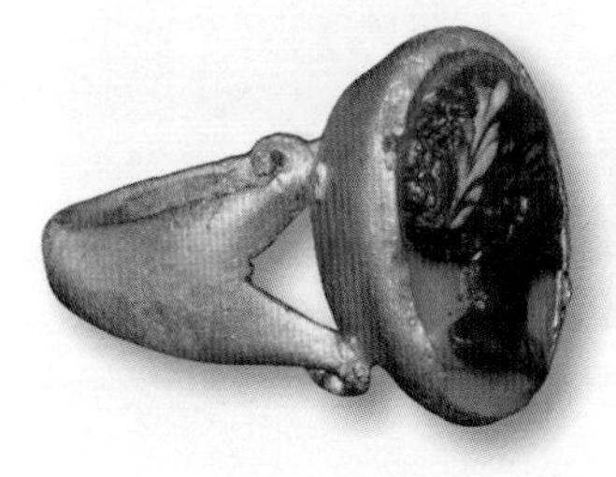
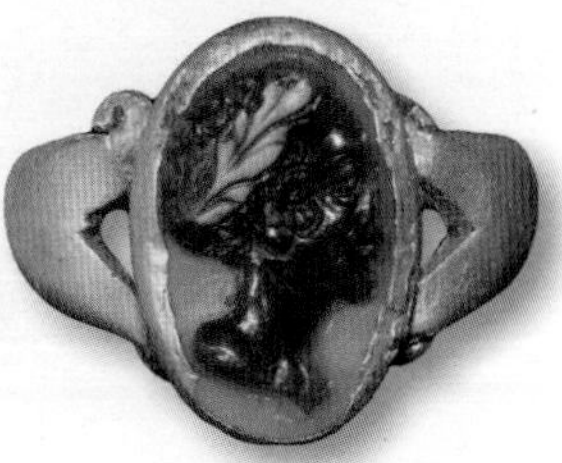

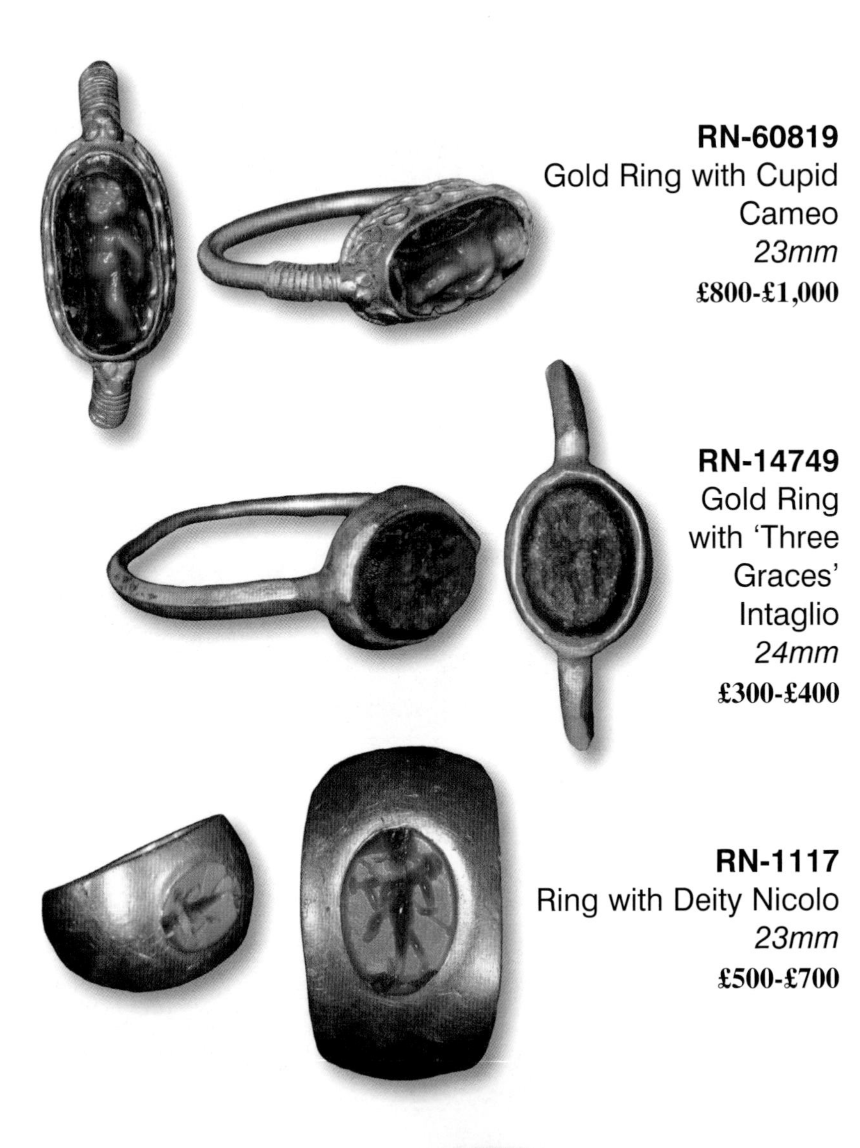

RN-60819
Gold Ring with Cupid Cameo
23mm
£800-£1,000

RN-14749
Gold Ring with 'Three Graces' Intaglio
24mm
£300-£400

RN-1117
Ring with Deity Nicolo
23mm
£500-£700

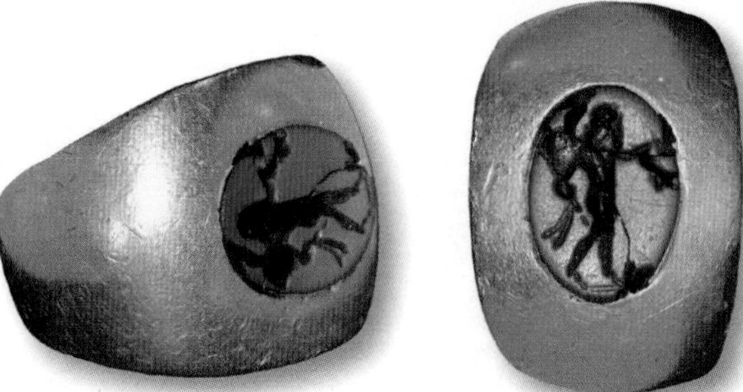

RN-57248
Gold Ring with Hercules Intaglio
21mm
£400-£600

RN-1798
Ring with Intaglio Bust
24mm
£400-£600

RN-38829
Gold Ring with
Bust Intaglio
19mm
£300-£400

RN-22748
Gold Ring
with Goddess
Intaglio
21mm
£200-£300

RN-34133
Gold Ring
16mm
Elliptical
sapphire
£200-£300

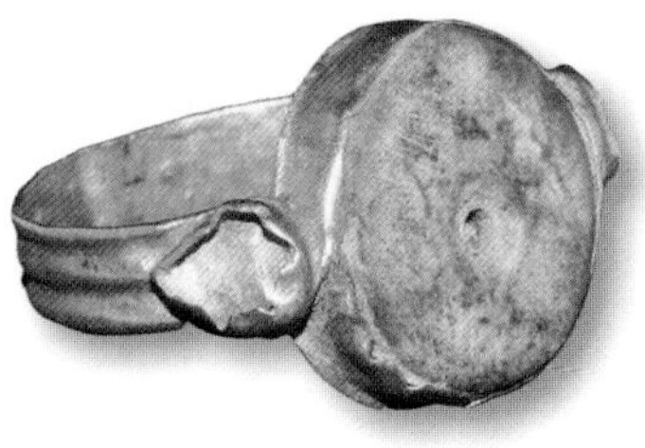
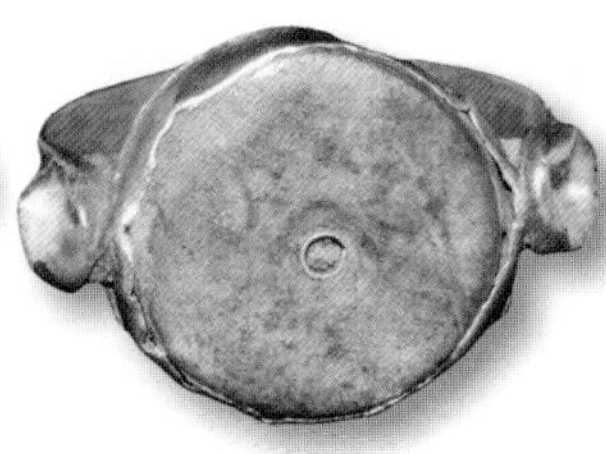

RN-29005
Gold Ring
16mm
Lapis lazuli cloison
£150-£200

RN-54751
Gold Ring with Bird Intaglio
21mm
£400-£600

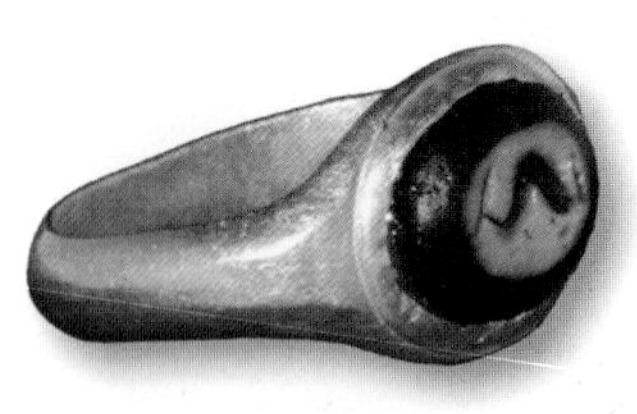

RN-45861
Gold Ring with Dolphin Intaglio
22mm
£300-£400

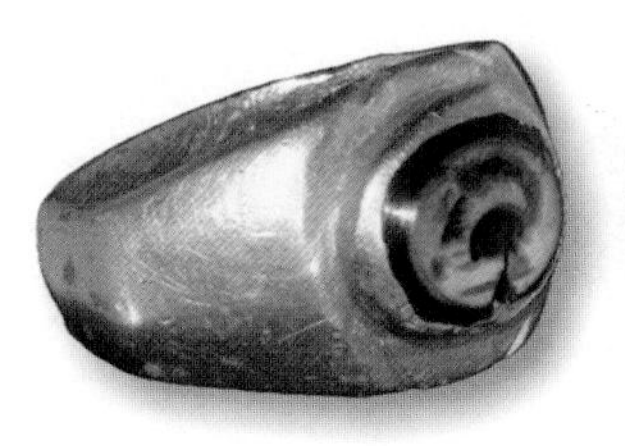
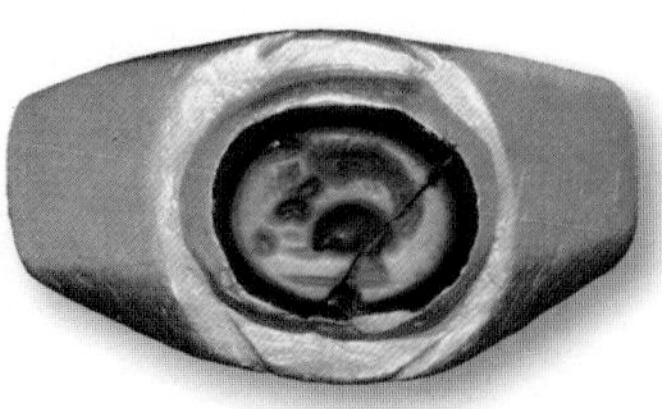

RN-14748
Gold Ring with Swan Intaglio
22mm
£400-£600

RN-62901
Gold Ring
21mm
Nicolo intaglio of Pisces (two fish)
£600-£800

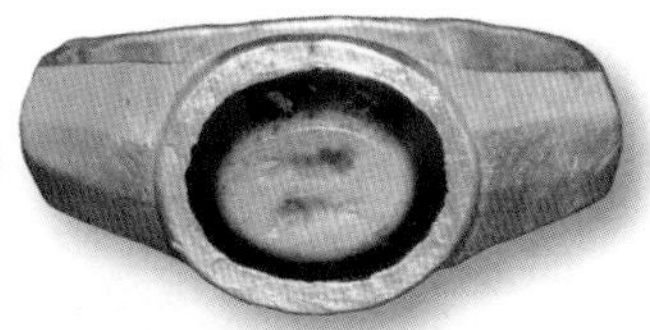

RN-52109
Gold Ring
18mm
With emerald cabochon
From £500

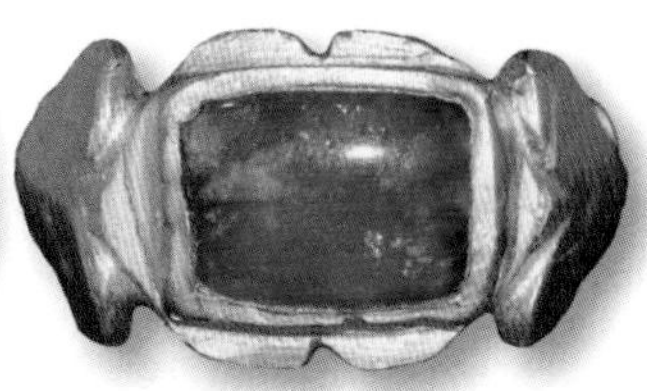

RN-53048
Gold Ring with Athena Parthenos Intaglio
17mm
£350-£450

RN-57251
Gold Ring with Victory Intaglio
23mm
£300-£400

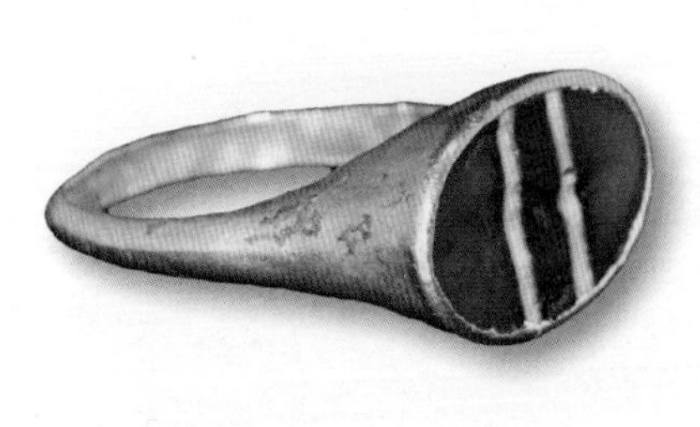

RN-21728
Gold
Ring with
Jasper
Intaglio of
Jupiter
22mm
£300-£400

RN-58913
Gold Ring
with Neptune
Intaglio
19mm
£300-£400

RN-54702
Gold Ring
with Bird
Intaglio
21mm
£300-£400

RN-57373
Gold Ring with
Female Bust Intaglio
26mm
£500-£700

RN-34176
Gold Intaglio Ring with Sol in Chariot
22mm
£400-£600

RN-12746
Gold Wreathed Bust Intaglio Ring
18mm
£400-£600

RN-51826
Gold Ring with Hippocampus Intaglio
23mm
£400-£600

RN-46458
Gold Ring with Eagle Intaglio
19mm
£300-£400

RN-10048
Gold Ring with
Harpocrates Intaglio
24mm
From £1,000

RN-52329
Gold Ring with
Cameo
23mm
£400-£600

RN-63937
Gold Ring with
Cockerel Intaglio
17mm
£300-£400

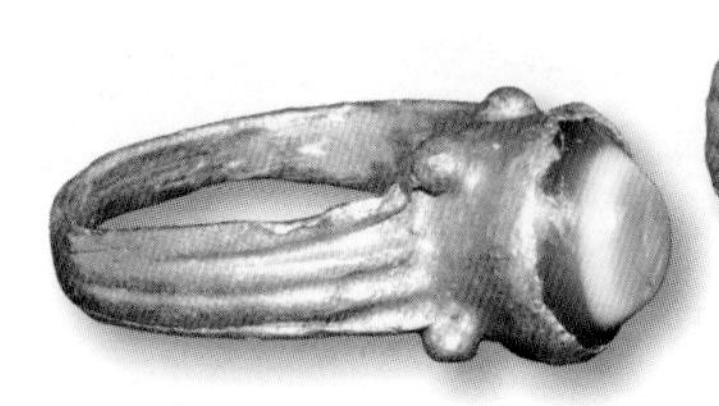

RN-23563
Gold Ring
23mm
Trophy on
onyx intaglio
£300-£400

RN-27613
Gold Openwork Finger Ring with Female Mask Intaglio
29mm
£800-£1,000

RN-37224
Gold Ring with Carved Bust
21mm
£800-£1,000

RN-35843
Gold Ring with Man and Goat Intaglio
18mm
£400-£600

RN-60444
Gold Ring with Eagle Intaglio
21mm
£400-£600

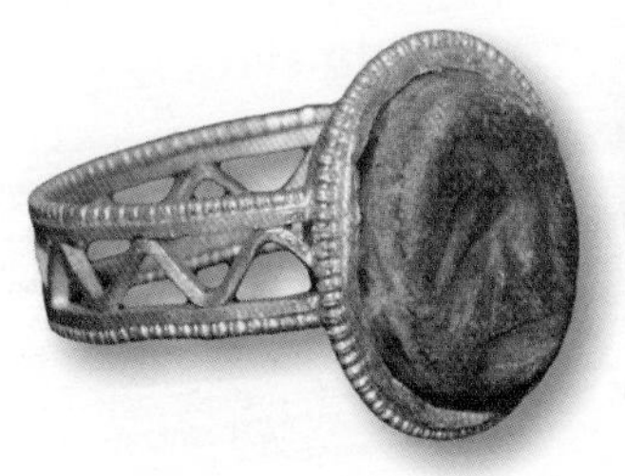

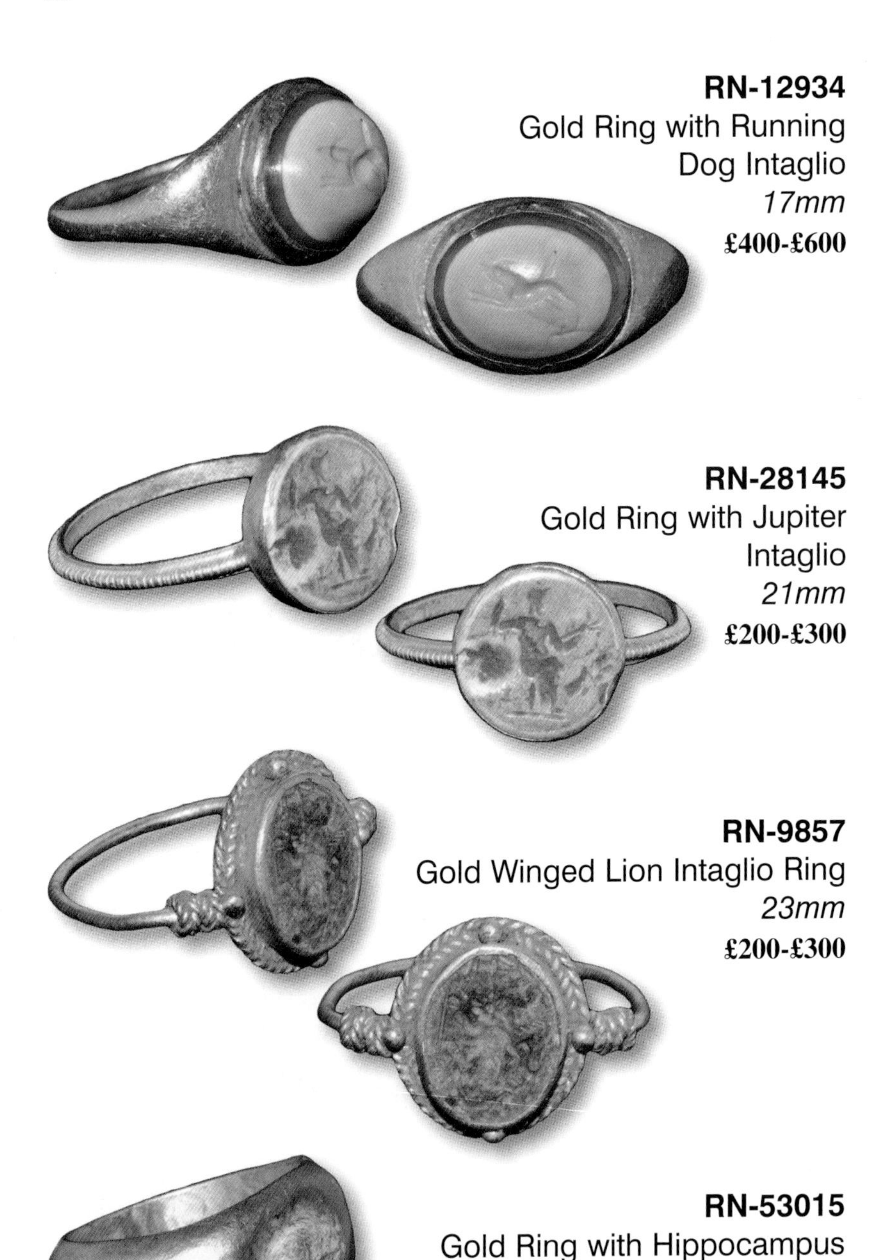

RN-12934
Gold Ring with Running Dog Intaglio
17mm
£400-£600

RN-28145
Gold Ring with Jupiter Intaglio
21mm
£200-£300

RN-9857
Gold Winged Lion Intaglio Ring
23mm
£200-£300

RN-53015
Gold Ring with Hippocampus Intaglio
21mm
£250-£350

RN-60454
Gold Ring
with Serpent
Intaglio
22mm
£400-£600

RN-56246
Gold Ring with
Altar Intaglio
20mm
£300-£400

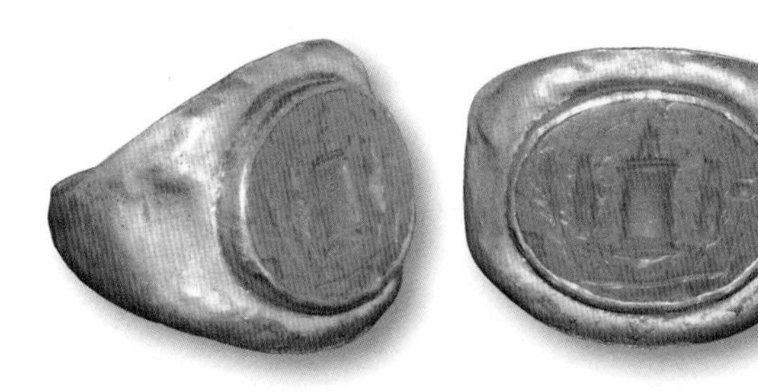

RN-35765
Gold Ring with Ram's Head
Intaglio
20mm
£300-£400

RN-30494
Gold Ring with
Maenad Intaglio
18mm
£250-£350

RN-65767

Inscribed Silver Seal Ring

23mm

Inscribed 'FIDES / LEGIONE / S.P.Q.R.' (Faithful to the Legion, Senate and Roman People)

£300-£400

RN-70547

Silver Ring with Inscription

26 mm

£150-£200

RN-67728

Silver Ring with Inscription

24 mm

£120-£170

RN-2737
Silver Ring
25mm
Inscribed DEO and INVICTO (to the unconquered god)
£150-£200

RN-21020
Silver TOT Ring
27mm
£200-£300

RN-60845
Inscribed Silver Ring
28mm
'IX' on each shoulder and bezel inscribed
'HISP' for Legio IX Hispana
£150-£200

RN-51798
Inscribed
Silver Ring
26mm
Greek text
'V? A ? V P
M H ? ?'
£150-£200

RN-57546
Inscribed Silver Ring
25mm
Inscribed 'V / ?EMIN / O' (for
Legio V Gemina)
£120-£180

RN-31122
Inscribed Silver Ring
27mm
Incised initials 'GA'
£100-£150

RN-28547
Silver Ring Bezel
29mm
Roman capitals 'DEO/MER'
£40-£60

RN-59530
Silver Clasped Hands Marriage Ring
20mm
£150-£200

RN-3303
Silver Fede
Marriage Ring
24mm
£150-£200

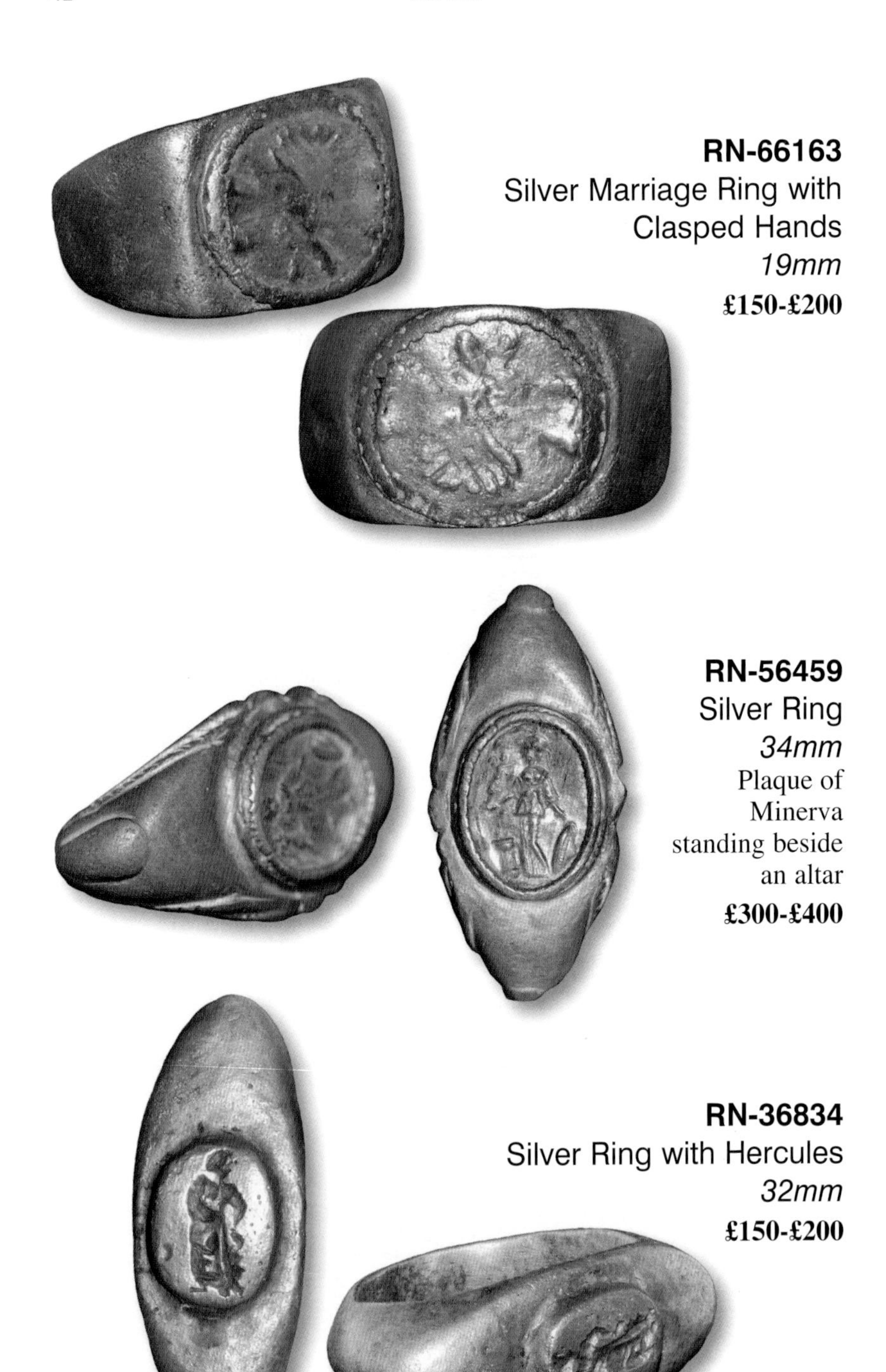

RN-66163
Silver Marriage Ring with Clasped Hands
19mm
£150-£200

RN-56459
Silver Ring
34mm
Plaque of Minerva standing beside an altar
£300-£400

RN-36834
Silver Ring with Hercules
32mm
£150-£200

RN-64773
Silver Ring
with Jupiter
22mm
£80-£100

RN-69783
Silver Ring with
Chi-Rho
22mm
£100-£140

RN-36841
Silver 'Palm Frond'
Intaglio Ring
25mm

£80-£100

RN-17108
Silver Key Finger Ring
20mm
£80-£100

RN-70548
Silver Snake Ring
26mm
£50-£70

RN-44958
Silver Snake Ring with Looped Tail
24mm
£80-£100

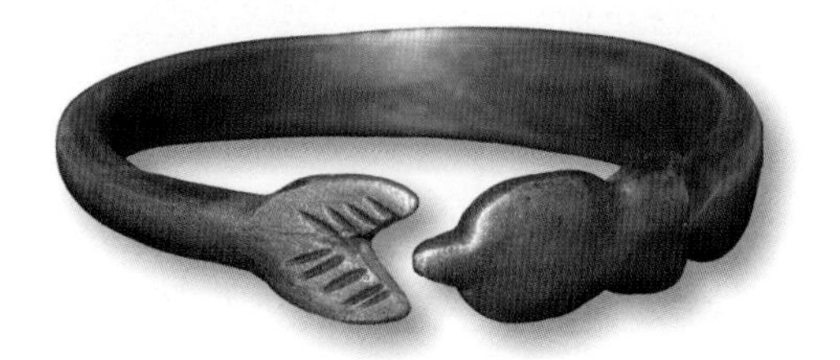

RN-67117
Silver Fish Ring
24 mm
£40-£60

RN-42439

Silver Ring with Carnelian

27mm

Eagle with wreath between two military standards

£400-£600

RN-12783

Silver Intaglio Ring

19mm

£120-£180

RN-42350

Ring with Fortuna

21mm

£100-£150

RN-14785

'Aelius Titus' Inscribed Ring

29mm

£60-£80

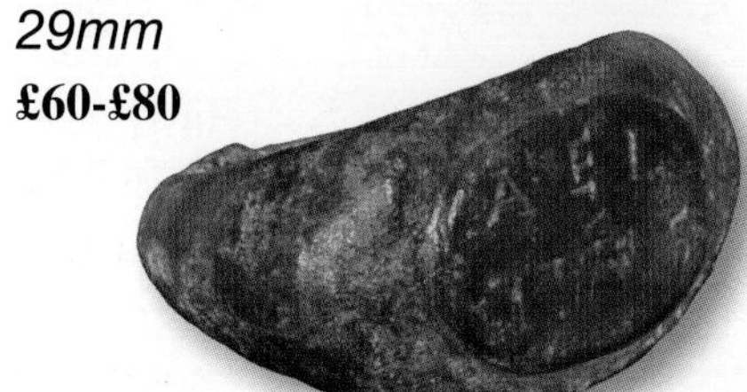

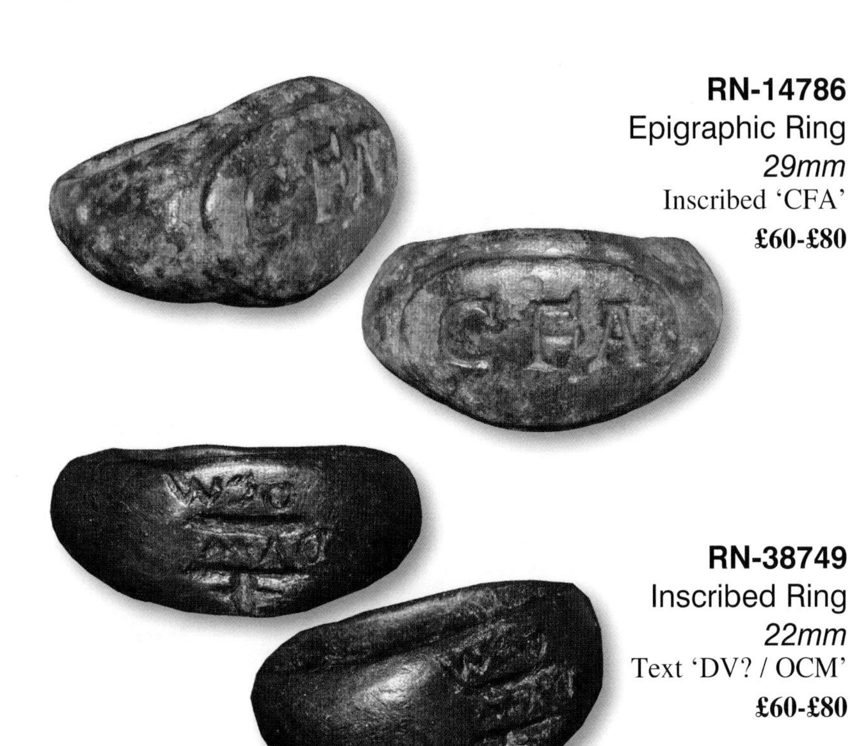

RN-14786
Epigraphic Ring
29mm
Inscribed 'CFA'
£60-£80

RN-38749
Inscribed Ring
22mm
Text 'DV? / OCM'
£60-£80

RN-30429
Ring with Imperial Bust
31mm
£50-£70

RN-40287
Seal
Ring with
Goddess
24mm
£60-£80

RN-41135
Seal Ring with Jupiter
17mm
£50-£70

RN-37185
Ring with Sol Invictus
27mm
£50-£70

RN-11268
Ring with Cameo Bust
21mm
£100-£150

RN-12905
Enamelled Finger Ring
21mm
£60-£80

RN-48014
Temple Seal
Ring
24mm
£80-£100

RN-22411
'Swastika'
Ring
21mm
£60-£80

RN-35773
Ring with
Jupiter's
Thunderbolt
Intaglio
21mm
£60-£80

RN-41837
Ring with
Apollo Intaglio
24mm
£200-£300

RN-36342
Ring with Female Bust
22mm
£120-£180

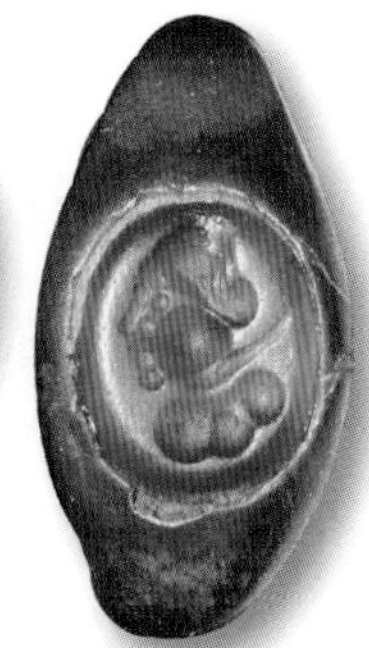

RN-18704
Ring with Female Bust Intaglio
23mm
£120-£180

RN-27636
Ring with Female Bust Intaglio
17mm
£100-£150

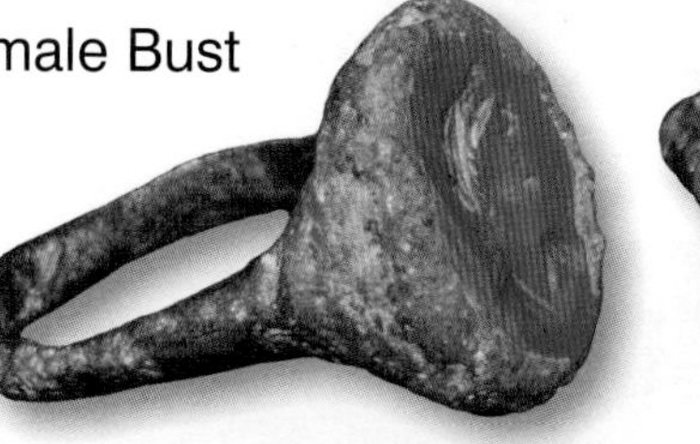

RN-42034
Ring with Winged Victory Intaglio
24mm
£100-150

RN-20528
Ring with Goddess Laetitia Intaglio
27mm
£200-£300

RN-38139
Gilt-Bronze Ring with Eagle Intaglio
33mm
£100-£150

RN-17031
Ring with Clasped Hands Intaglio
19mm
£80-£100

RN-36343
Ring with Mercury Intaglio
23mm
£60-£80

RN-11889
Intaglio Finger Ring
25mm
£60-£80

RN-64810
Intaglio of
Marcus Junius
Brutus
30mm
£4,000-£6,000

RN-53893
Ring Intaglio
26mm
Judgment of Paris
£100-£150

RN-64806
Amber Ring with
Cupid Intaglio
34mm
£200-£300

AB-23467
Silver Bird Brooch
31mm
Modelled in the round
£60-£80

AB-4973
Silver Enamelled Bird Brooch
46mm
With flared tail and enamel details
£60-£80

AB-1130
Enamelled Flying Bird Brooch
40mm
Enamelled panels to the tail and wings
£120-£180

AB-20469
Enamelled Bird Brooch
33mm
Enamelled detail to the wings
£30-£50

AB-20478
Bird Brooch
40mm
Enamelled panels to the wings and body
£30-£50

AB-17103
Bird Brooch
24mm
Feather texture to the wings
£60-£80

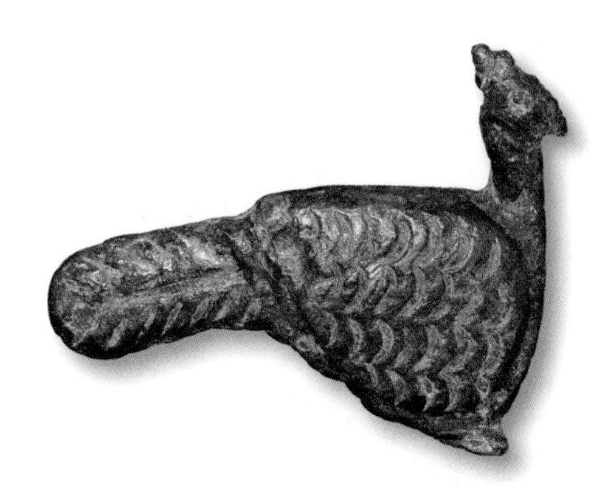

AB-64693
Bird Brooch
26mm
Fanned tail and raised head
£40-£60

AB-48825
Bird Brooch
34mm
Notch detailing to wings and tail
£30-£50

AB-18549
Bird Brooch
35mm
Raised head and small wings
£30-£50

AB-37295
Flying Bird Brooch
36mm
Loop beneath the tail for a securing thong or chain
£30-£50

AB-13674
Bird Brooch
38mm
Hatched body and ring-and-dot motif
£40-£60

AB-15117
Bird Brooch
35mm
Enamel discs on the wings
£40-£60

AB-52187
Bird Brooch
24mm
Punched detail on the wings
£40-£60

AB-65938
Bird Brooch
35mm
Fan shaped tail and
incised line for the beak
£40-£60

AB-52188
Bird Brooch
37mm
Modelled in the round,
flat tail
£50-£70

AB-64691
Bird Brooch
35mm
Modelled in the round
£40-£60

AB-41817
Bird Brooch
42mm
Incised bands to the neck and rear body
£60-£80

AB-33950
Bird Brooch
47mm
Head facing to the rear
£80-£100

AB-17102
Bird Brooch
61mm with pin
Profile body and head
£40-£60

AB-11273
Tinned Bronze Bird Brooch
36mm
Body in plan, head raised
£80-£100

AB-15113
Bird Brooch
32mm
Curved neck and spread wings
£40-£60

AB-52190
Eagle Brooch
31mm
Curved neck and spread wings
£50-£70

AB-60449
Eagle Brooch
33mm
Triangle on the chest and incised circles on the wings and tail
£50-£70

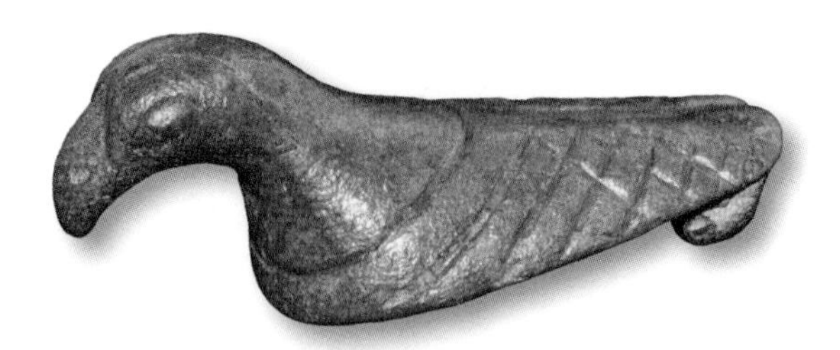

AB-3679
Eagle Brooch
45mm
Modelled in the round
£60-£80

AB-42076
Peacock Plate Brooch
36mm
In profile with wings extended
£50-£80

AB-14492
Peacock Plate Brooch
26mm
Tail spread
£80-£100

AB-4077
Silvered Peacock Brooch
22mm
Tail spread
£80-£100

AB-16143
Enamelled Peacock Brooch
40mm
Enamel pellets on the tail
£80-£100

AB-14446
Enamelled Cockerel Brooch
25mm
Enamel on the chest
£120-£180

AB-4069
Enamelled Owl Brooch
30mm
Enamelled eyes
£200-£300

AB-63019
Enamelled Duck in Flight Brooch
35mm
Enamel panels on the wings
£150-£200

AB-8732
Enamelled Swan Brooch
30mm
£150-£200

AB-2352
Enamelled Swan Brooch
34mm
Enamelled panels on the flanks
£100-£150

AB-4145
Silver Boar Brooch
78mm
Inscribed '+ ANDIAT' for the owner Andiatus
From £3,000

AB-34181
Enamelled Boar Brooch
39mm
Enamelled pellets on the flanks
£200-£300

AB-4070
Enamelled Boar Brooch
37mm
Standing on a baseline
£120-£180

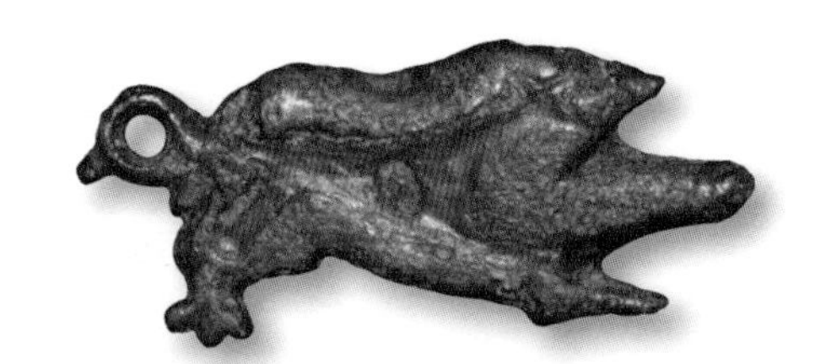

AB-2613
Boar Brooch with Enamel
31mm
Looped tail
£80-£100

AB-14457
Boar Plate Brooch
44mm
Standing on a baseline
£100-£150

AB-59033
Silver Boar Brooch
37mm
Running on a baseline
£100-£150

AB-50587
Boar Brooch
33mm
Profile outline
£50-£70

AB-63765
Silver-Gilt Openwork Cicada Brooch
41mm
Pierced wings
£200-£300

AB-31714
Cicada Brooch
84mm
Triangular wings
£100-£150

AB-37306
Tinned Bronze Cicada Brooch
35mm
Tinning on the wings and body
£80-£100

AB-28762
Cicada Brooch
40mm
£40-£60

AB-11665
Cicada Brooch
37mm
Curved wings
£50-£80

AB-8575
Silver Fly Brooch
24mm
Triangular wings and gusseted neck
£100-£150

AB-59277
Fly Plate Brooch
35mm
Slender D-section body
£80-£100

AB-16142
Enamelled Fly Brooch
50mm
Polychrome enamel panels
£50-£80

AB-47679
Silver Horse and Rider Brooch
33mm
Prancing horse on a baseline
£200-£300

AB-52191
Enamelled Horse and Rider Brooch
33mm
Rider leaning backwards
£120-£180

AB-30331
Enamelled Horse and Rider Brooch
24mm
With enamel panels
£80-£100

AB-23223
Silver Enamelled Horse Brooch
36mm
Enamelled panels and roundel on the chest
£200-£300

AB-23224
Silver Enamelled Horse Brooch
43mm
Enamelled panels and eye
£200-£300

AB-27768
Horse Brooch
34mm
Galloping posture
£150-£200

AB-7416
Enamelled Horse Plate Brooch
34mm
Contoured shoulders, enamelled panels
£150-£200

AB-4074
Silvered Horse Brooch
28mm
Roundel to the shoulder
£100-£150

AB-37305
Decorated Horse Brooch
34mm
Pierced neck indicating the bridle
£100-£150

AB-24858
Horse Plate Brooch
34mm
Galloping posture
£60-£80

AB-11662
Horse Plate Brooch
41mm
Walking posture on baseline
£50-£70

AB-35798
Horse Brooch
37mm
Thick baseline
£50-£70

AB-62870
Horse Plate Brooch
30mm
Grazing posture on baseline
£50-£70

AB-57641
Horse Plate
Brooch
35mm
Grazing posture
£50-£70

AB-31130
Horse Brooch
31mm
One foreleg raised
£80-£100

AB-31131
Horse Brooch
35mm
Saddled, on a baseline
£80-£100

AB-16324
Silver Horse Bow
Brooch
53mm
Saddle bow modelled on
the shoulder
£80-£100

AB-2493
Horse Plate Brooch
36mm
Saddle detail to the flank
£60-£80

AB-46472
Horse Heads Plate Brooch
26mm
Horse heads flanking a vertical bar
£50-£70

AB-50585
Horse Plate Brooch
34mm
Running on a baseline
£50-£70

AB-12748
Silver Horse Bow Brooch
36mm
Modelled in the round
£200-£300

AB-48822
Horse Bow Brooch
45mm
Rear legs forming the headplate
£100-£150

AB-48823
Gilt Horse Bow Brooch
39mm
Sprung pin
£80-£100

AB-48827
Horse Bow Brooch
51mm
Catch below the forelegs
£80-£100

AB-42077
Horse Brooch
47mm
Hinged pin
£60-£80

AB-48824
Horse Bow Brooch
38mm
Hinged pin, bridle detail to the head
£60-£80

AB-11664
Horse Bow Brooch
47mm
Hinged pin curved neck
£50-£70

AB-48826
Horse Bow Brooch
34mm
£50-£70

AB-64696
Twin Horses Bow Brooch
37mm
Foreparts of two horses
£40-£60

AB-28779
Horse Bow Brooch
39mm
Sprung pin
£30-£50

AB-46476
Horse Heads Plate Brooch
40mm
Radiating horse heads
£50-£80

AB-4810
Horse-Heads Plate Brooch
41mm
Ring-and-dot eyes
£50-£80

AB-8210
Horse-Heads Plate Brooch
34mm
Notched mane detailing
£50-£70

AB-10870
Horse-Heads Plate Brooch
36mm
£40-£60

AB-18547
Horse-Heads Plate Brooch
34mm
£40-£60

AB-10023
Horse-Heads Plate Brooch
36mm
£50-£70

AB-2538
Silver Dolphin Bow Brooch
33mm
Curved body with fin detail
£150-£200

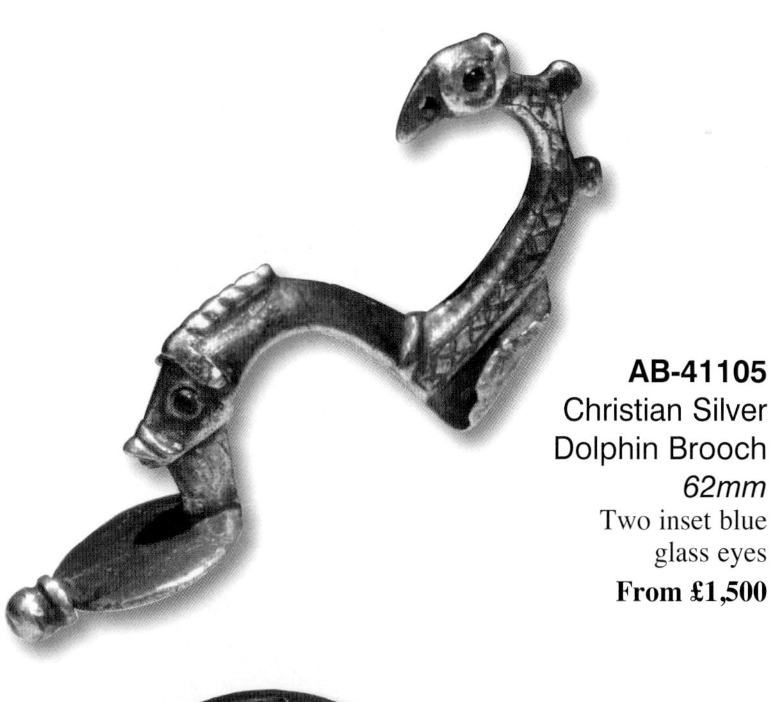

AB-41105
Christian Silver
Dolphin Brooch
62mm
Two inset blue
glass eyes
From £1,500

AB-10385
Enamelled
Polychrome Brooch
with Dolphin
51mm
Dolphin figurine
modelled in the round
From £1,000

AB-64777
Double Silver Dolphin Bow Brooch
28mm
Two dolphins parallel
£120-£180

AB-1104
Silver Dolphin Brooch
37mm
Knee brooch with dolphin details
£100-£150

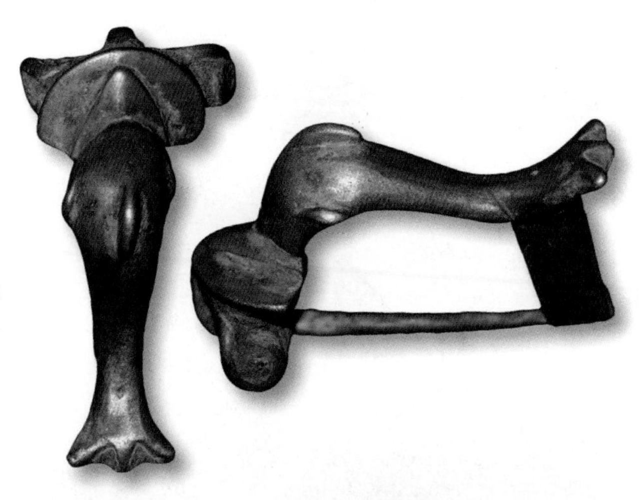

AB-30493
Plate Brooch
30mm
Cupid riding dolphin
£80-£100

AB-42078
Silvered Dolphin Brooch
35mm
£40-£60

AB-57666
Twin-Dolphin Bow Brooch
32mm
Two dolphins parallel
£60-£80

AB-41819
Double Dolphin Brooch
28mm
Two dolphins parallel and curved headplate
£40-£60

AB-4081
Urn and
Dolphins Plate
Brooch
29mm
Romano-British
type
£80-£100

AB-63063
Urn and
Dolphins Plate
Brooch
29mm
£50-£70

AB-17104
Dolphins and Mask
Plate Brooch
30mm
Romano-British
type
£40-£60

AB-66172
Silver Crayfish Brooch
47mm
Parcel-gilt surface
From £600

AB-14488
Silvered Fish Plate Brooch
42mm
Flatfish type
£100-£150

AB-59284
Fish Brooch
36mm
Enamelled details
£40-£60

AB-69632
Enamelled Fish Brooch
45mm
Bronze with red enamel detail
£40-£60

AB-32341
Silver Leopard Brooch
41mm
Enamelled spots
£300-£400

AB-37303
Panther Brooch
43mm
Enamelled blue and white spots
£200-£300

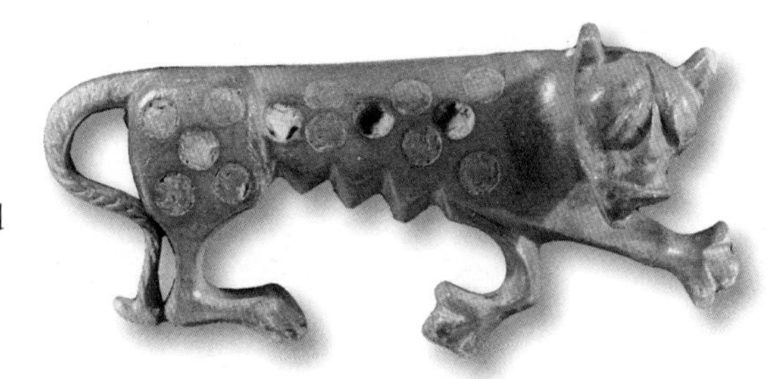

AB-12911
Enamelled Panther Brooch
42mm
Enamelled red and white spots
£200-£300

AB-4072
Enamelled Panther Brooch
37mm
Enamelled red and white spots
£100-£150

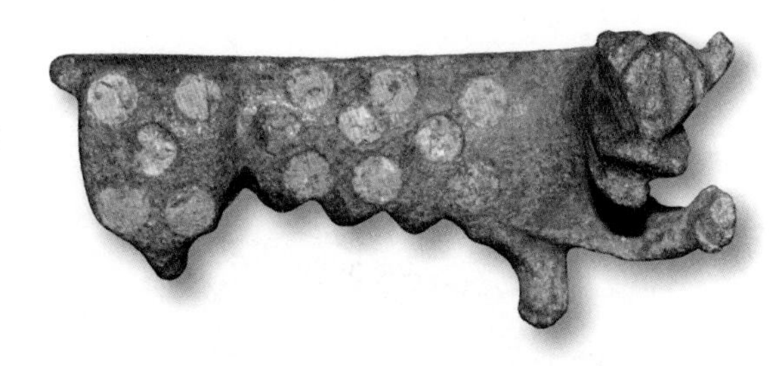

AB-4071
Enamelled Panther Brooch
34mm
£150-£200

AB-50518
Bow Brooch with Panther Terminal
54mm
Trumpet-derivative type
£150-£200

AB-65296
Panther Plate Brooch
40mm
Profile on a baseline
£50-£70

AB-20227
Panther Brooch
35mm
Crouching profile on a baseline
£40-£60

AB-3684
Lioness Plate Brooch
46mm
Advancing on a baseline
£120-£180

AB-5705
Lion Plate Brooch
33mm
With detailed mane, on a baseline
£80-£100

AB-63062
Lion Plate Brooch
38mm
Advancing on a baseline
£70-£90

AB-4936
Lion Plate Brooch
36mm
Leaping stance
£60-£80

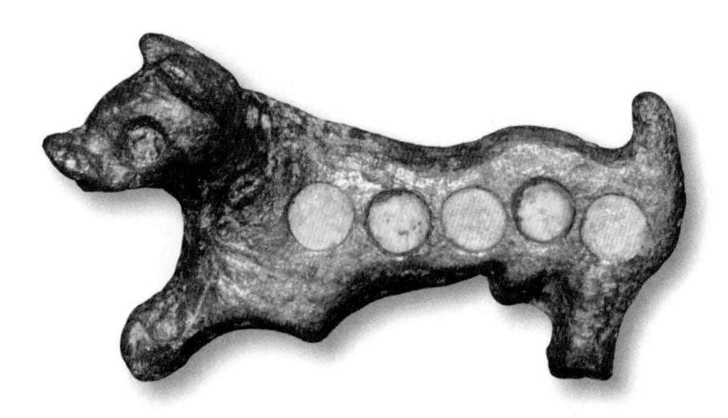

AB-4075
Enamelled Wolf Brooch
28mm
Romano-British type
£80-£100

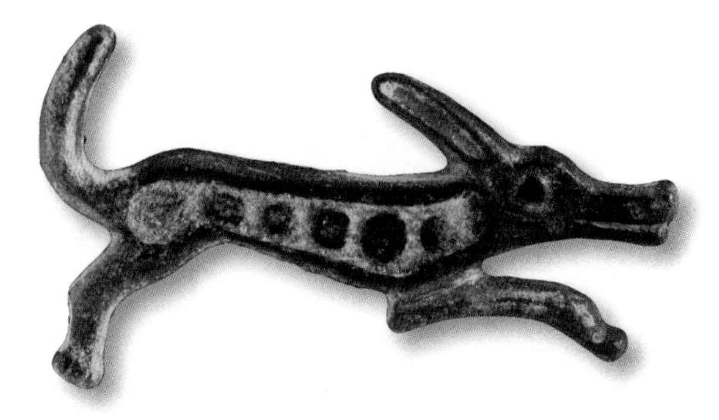

AB-14472
Running Dog Plate Brooch
39mm
Enamelled flank
£150-£200

AB-31925
Silver Dog Plate Brooch
29mm
Sitting stance
£200-£300

AB-51816
Enamelled Hound Brooch
42mm
Running stance
£100-£150

AB-11948
Dog Plate Brooch
38mm
Standing on a baseline
£50-£70

AB-23228
Silver Hare and Hound Brooch
41mm
Hare fleeing a hound on a baseline
£150-£200

AB-59280
Twin Hound-and-Hare Brooch
36mm
Hare-and-hound motif reflected round a median baseline
£80-£100

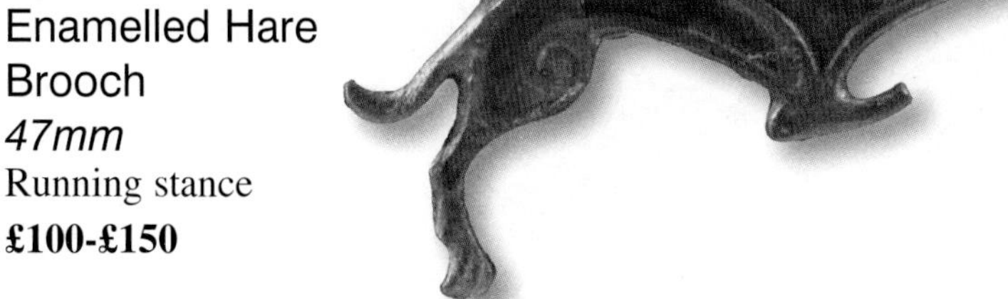

AB-8615
Enamelled Hare Brooch
47mm
Running stance
£100-£150

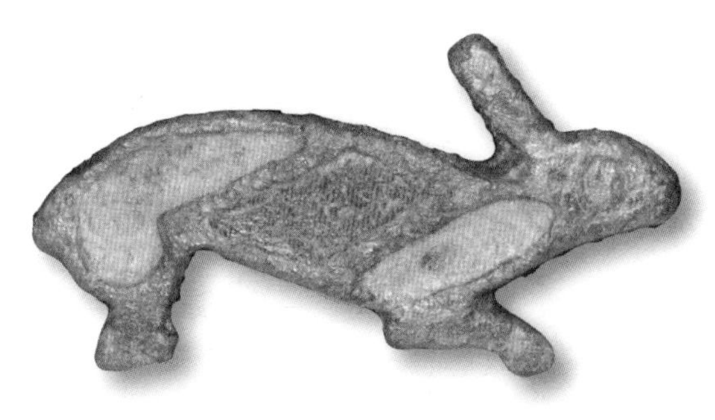

AB-8758
Enamelled Hare Brooch
31mm
Enamelled panel to the flank
£80-£100

AB-4076
Enamelled Hare Brooch
25mm
Multiple triangular enamelled panels
£80-£100

AB-57524
Enamelled Hare Brooch
23mm
Multiple triangular enamelled panels
£70-£90

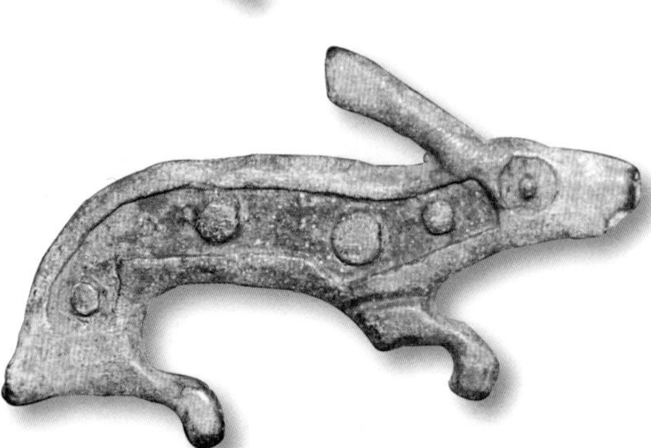

AB-17164
Hare Brooch
47mm
Running stance
£50-£70

AB-15126
Enamelled Hare
Brooch
23mm
Polychrome enamel panels
£50-£70

AB-10018
Silver Hare
Brooch
20mm
Niello stripes
£40-£60

AB-1131
Enamelled
Hippocampus
Brooch
52mm
Polychrome
enamel panels
From £400

AB-37304
Enamelled
Hippocampus
Brooch
49mm
Polychrome
enamel panels
From £300

AB-20952
Hippocampus
Brooch
57mm
Roundel to
the shoulder
£150-£200

AB-4875
Hippocampus
Brooch
38mm
Openwork mane
£80-£100

AB-4078
Enamelled
Hippocampus
Brooch
27mm
Enamel eye
£80-£100

AB-57523
Enamelled
Gryphon Brooch
50mm
Extended wing
to the back
From £300

AB-1124
Enamelled Frog
Brooch
38mm
Enamelled panels
and studs
From £300

AB-3518
Enamelled Frog Brooch
36mm
Enamelled panels and studs
£200-£300

AB-59396
Enamelled Frog Brooch
31mm
Triangular enamelled panels
£100-£150

AB-8458
Crocodile Brooch
65mm
Textured back
£120-£180

AB-3932
Reindeer Plate Brooch
40mm
Advancing on a baseline
£100-£150

AB-10017
Stag Plate
Brooch
34mm
Ring-and-dot motifs
£50-£80

AB-38695
Enamelled Hind's Head
Brooch
23mm
Leaf-shaped ears, enamelled
panel on the neck
£100-£150

AB-11904
Enamelled Bull Brooch
33mm
Head modelled in the round
£150-£200

AB-57676
Bull plate Brooch
34mm
Standing on a baseline
£80-£100

AB-3755
Bull Plate Brooch
36mm
Enamel roundels
£100-£150

AB-4079
Enamelled Deer Brooch
38mm
Advancing with head thrown back
£80-£100

AB-37293
Enamelled Zoomorphic Brooch
38mm
Disc body with animal-head terminal
£80-£100

AB-20228
Enamelled
Brooch
34mm
Hinged pin
on headplate
£40-£60

AB-42079
Hinge-Headed Brooch
43mm
Animal-head footplate
£30-£40

BB-42431
Gold Crossbow
Brooch
54mm
Openwork bow
and footplate
£1,500-£2,000

BB-35839
Gold Crossbow
Brooch
42mm
Onion-shaped
knops
£1,500-£2,000

BB-1110
Gold Crossbow Brooch
40mm
Granule detailing
£1,200-£1,800

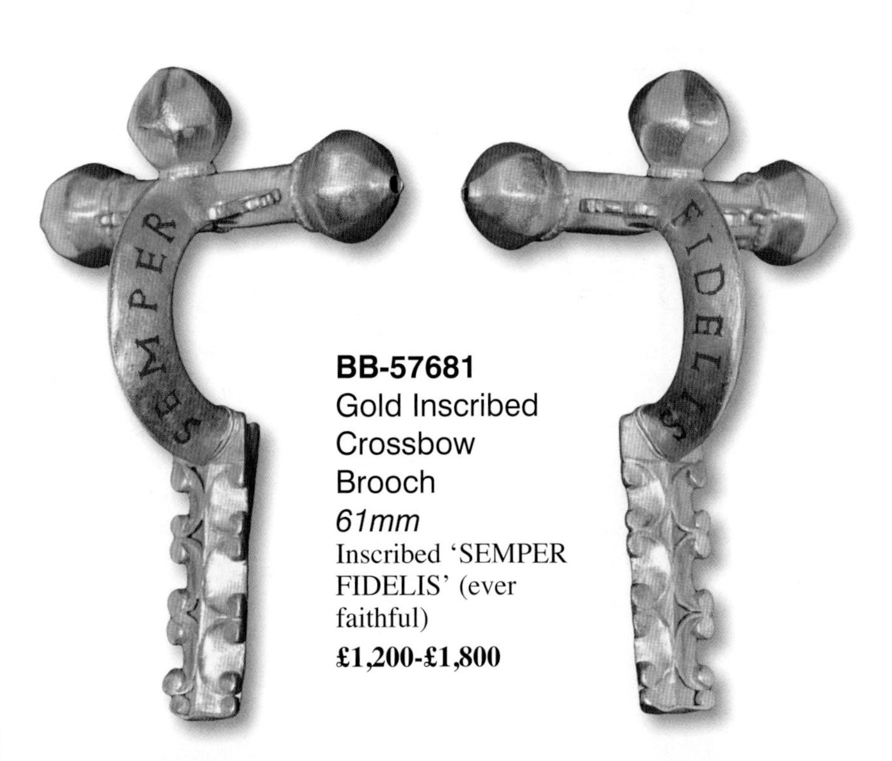

BB-57681
Gold Inscribed Crossbow Brooch
61mm
Inscribed 'SEMPER FIDELIS' (ever faithful)
£1,200-£1,800

BB-19280
Gold Crossbow Brooch
37mm
With niello
£800-£1,200

BB-30471
Silver Crossbow Brooch
64mm
Niello-inlaid text 'SPES ... BONA' (good hope)
£300-£400

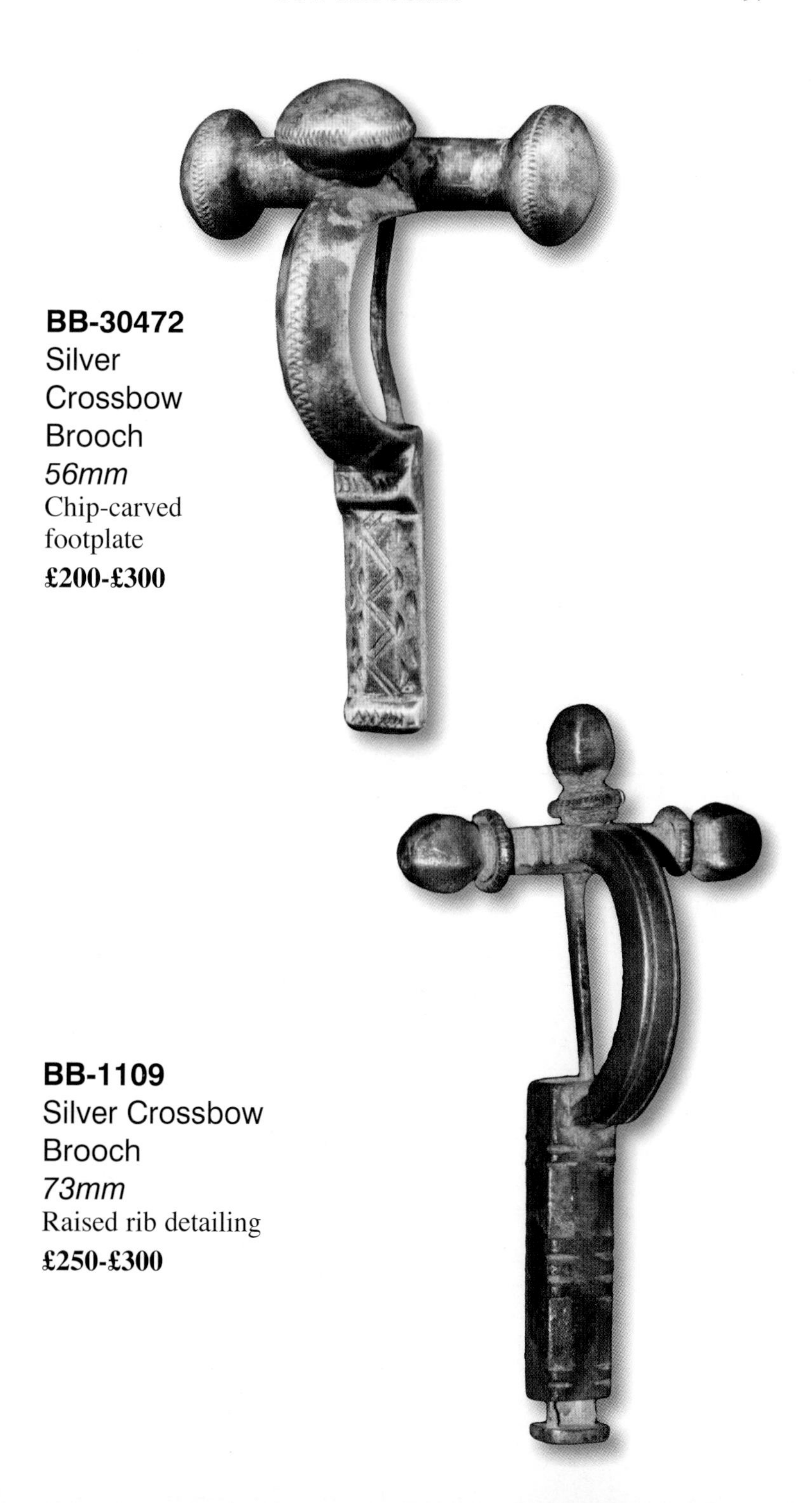

BB-30472
Silver
Crossbow
Brooch
56mm
Chip-carved
footplate
£200-£300

BB-1109
Silver Crossbow
Brooch
73mm
Raised rib detailing
£250-£300

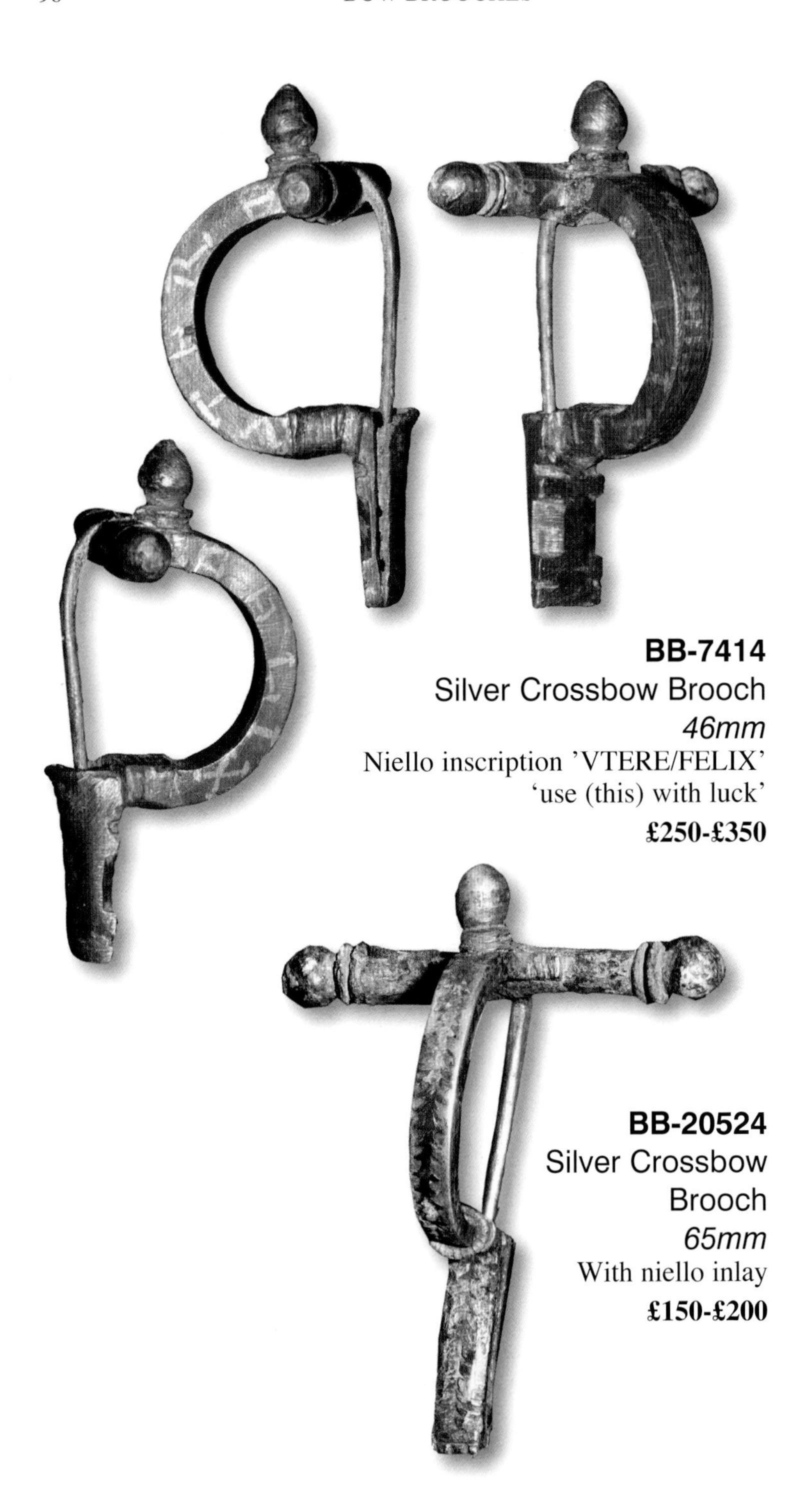

BB-7414
Silver Crossbow Brooch
46mm
Niello inscription 'VTERE/FELIX'
'use (this) with luck'
£250-£350

BB-20524
Silver Crossbow
Brooch
65mm
With niello inlay
£150-£200

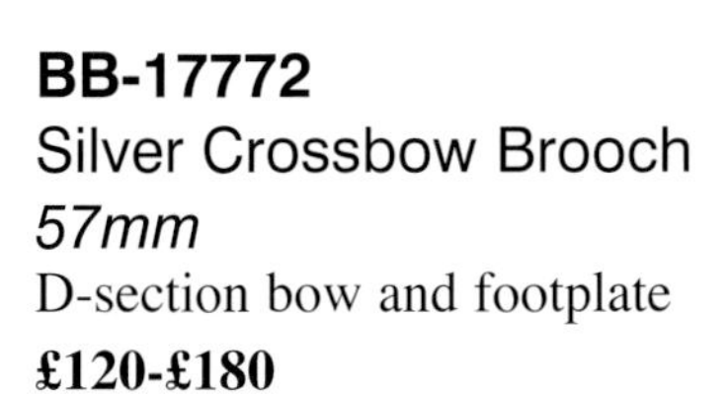

BB-17772
Silver Crossbow Brooch
57mm
D-section bow and footplate
£120-£180

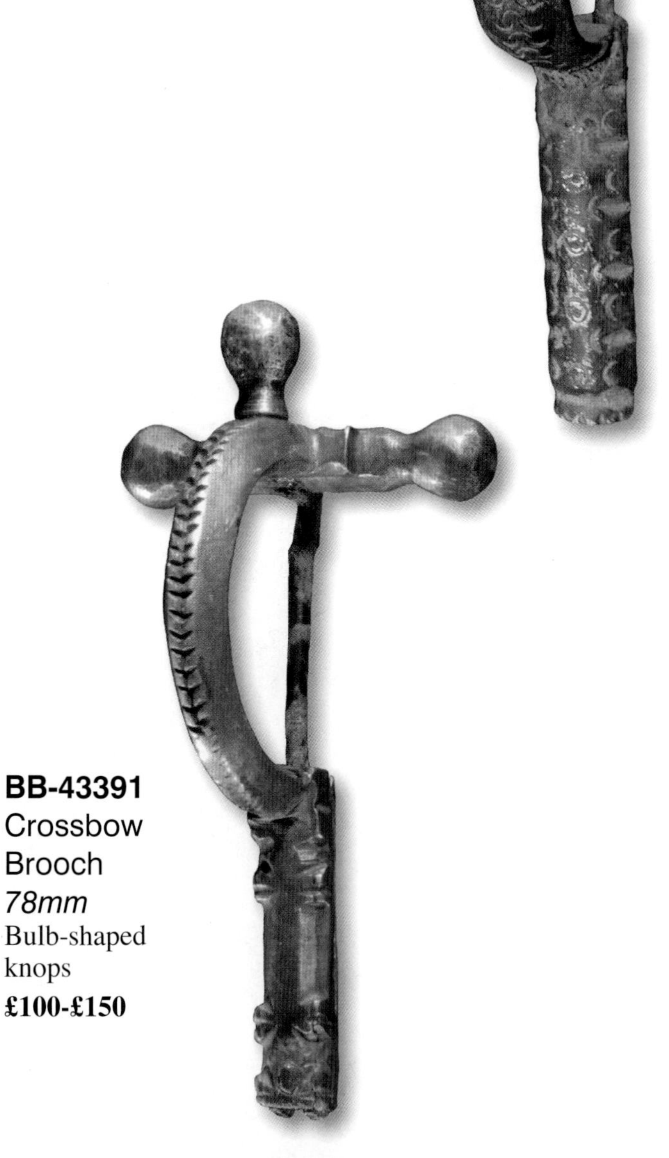

BB-43391
Crossbow
Brooch
78mm
Bulb-shaped
knops
£100-£150

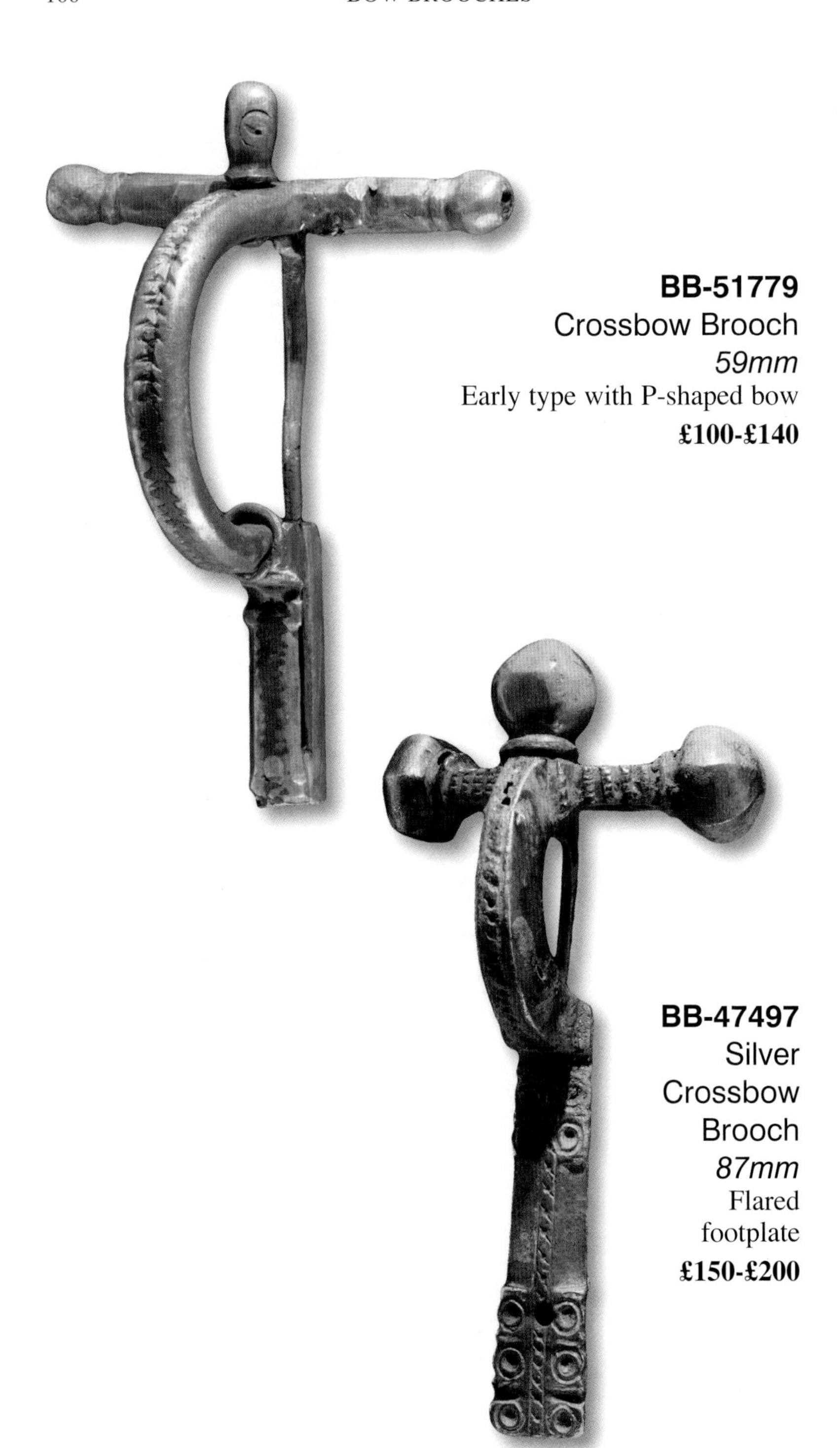

BB-51779
Crossbow Brooch
59mm
Early type with P-shaped bow
£100-£140

BB-47497
Silver
Crossbow
Brooch
87mm
Flared
footplate
£150-£200

BB-41106
Silver Bow Brooch
73mm
Angular P-shaped type
£200-£300

BB-45937
Bow
Brooch
64mm
Bifurcated
bow, leaf-
shaped foot
£150-£200

BB-42108
Silver Bow Brooch
46mm
Returned catch on the footplate
£80-£100

BB-48828
P-Shaped
Silver Bow
Brooch
67mm
Collars to
the bow
£100-£150

BB-52196
Silver Bow
Brooch
49mm
Kräftig
Profilierte type
£120-£180

BB-782
Silver 'Anchor' Bow Brooch
53mm
Kräftig Profilierte type
£100-£150

BB-23998
Silver Bow
Brooch
85mm
Flügelfibel type
From £300

BB-37223
Silver Openwork
Brooch
90mm
Flügelfibel type
From £300

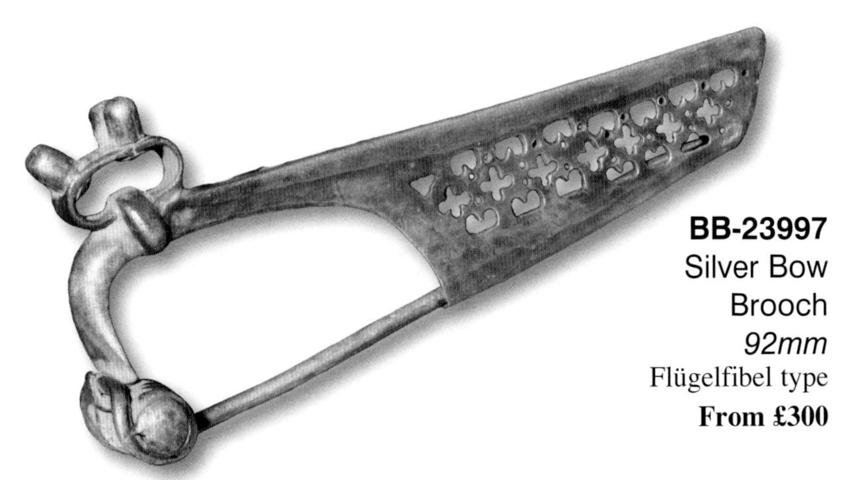

BB-23997
Silver Bow
Brooch
92mm
Flügelfibel type
From £300

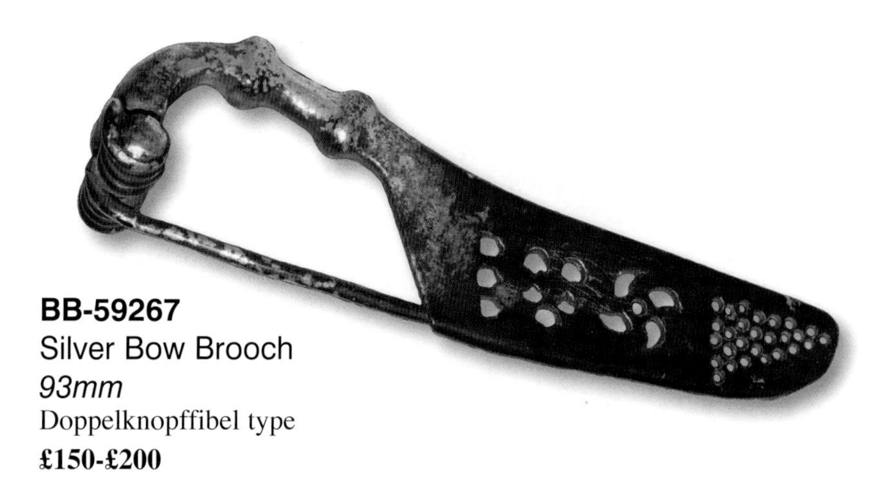

BB-59267
Silver Bow Brooch
93mm
Doppelknopffibel type
£150-£200

BB-57639
Silver Bow
Brooch
90mm
Bulbs on the
returned foot
£150-£200

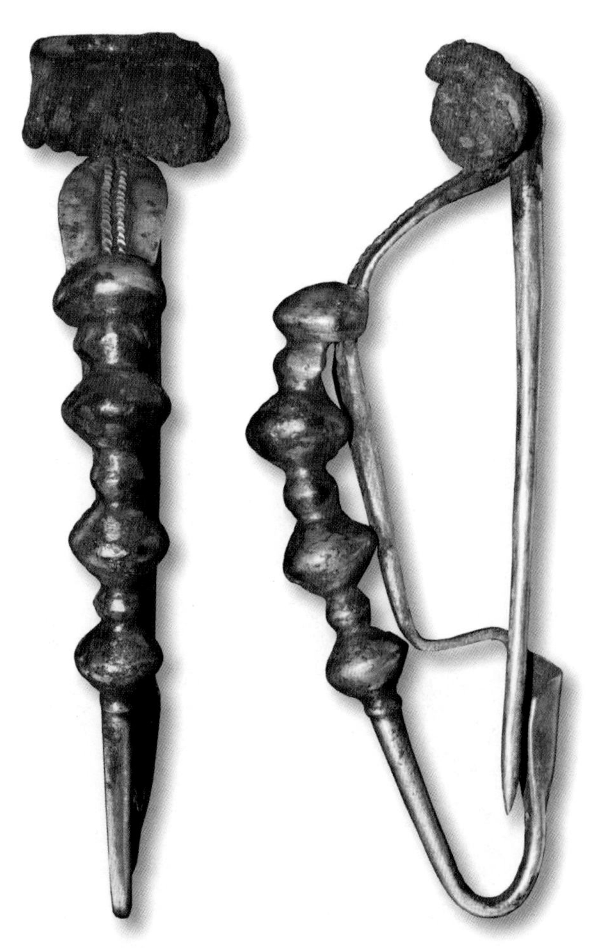

BB-42255
Silver Bow Brooch
with Wire
52mm
Ornamental link attached
to the headplate
£100-£150

BB-1912
Silver Bow
Brooch
55mm
P-shaped type
£120-£180

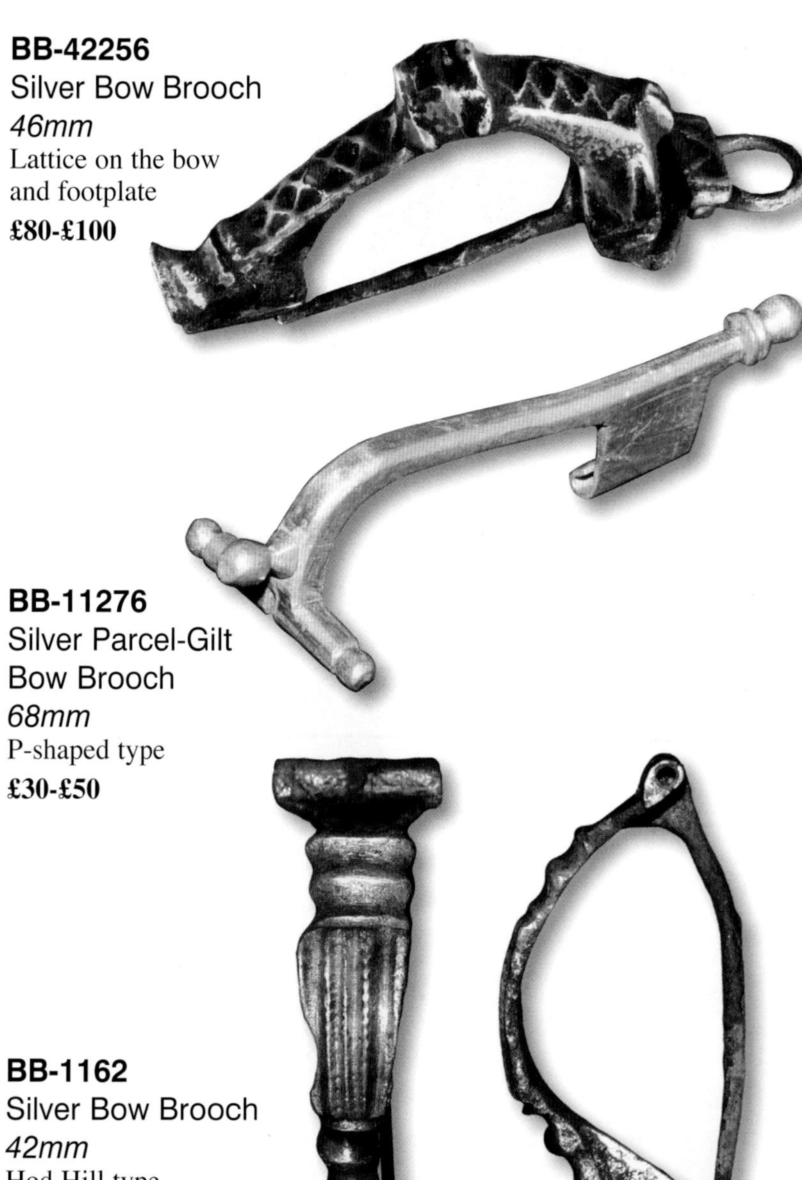

BB-42256
Silver Bow Brooch
46mm
Lattice on the bow and footplate
£80-£100

BB-11276
Silver Parcel-Gilt Bow Brooch
68mm
P-shaped type
£30-£50

BB-1162
Silver Bow Brooch
42mm
Hod Hill type
£80-£100

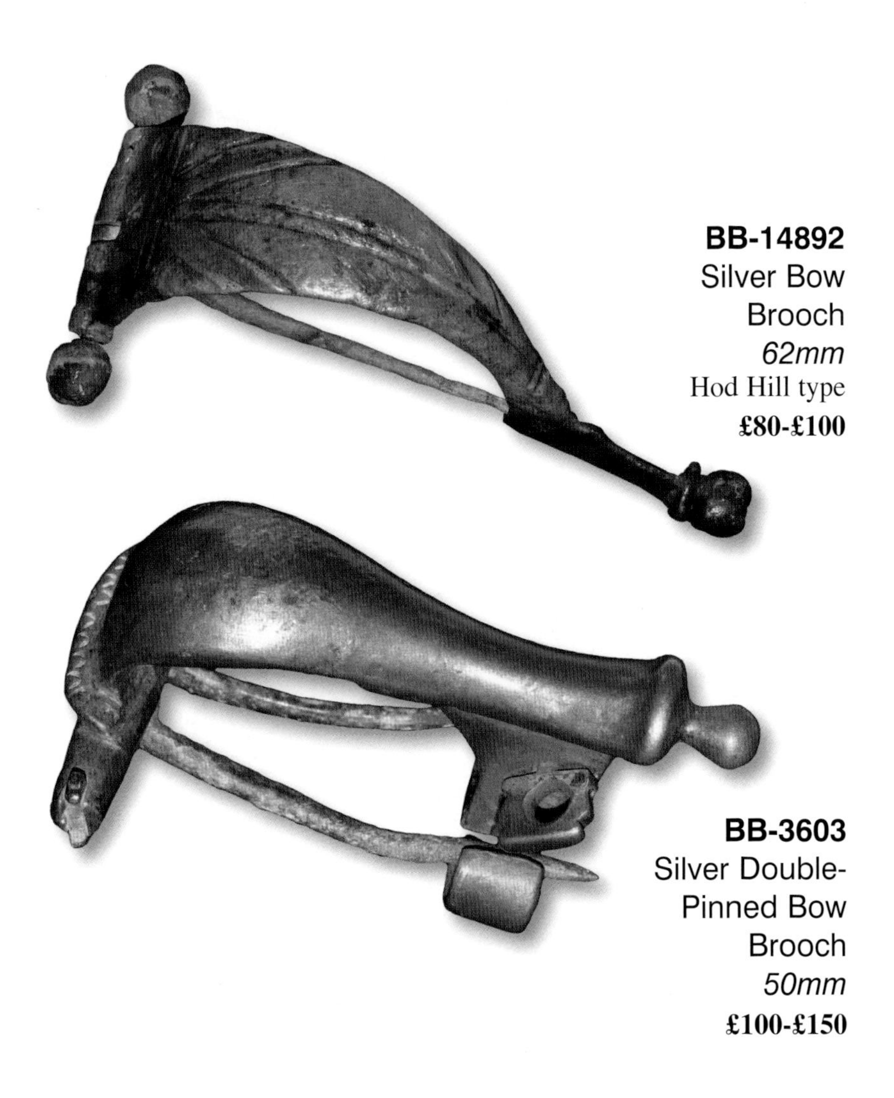

BB-14892
Silver Bow Brooch
62mm
Hod Hill type
£80-£100

BB-3603
Silver Double-Pinned Bow Brooch
50mm
£100-£150

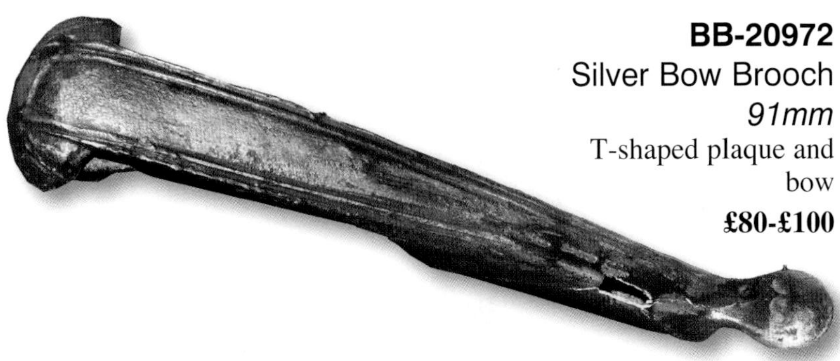

BB-20972
Silver Bow Brooch
91mm
T-shaped plaque and bow
£80-£100

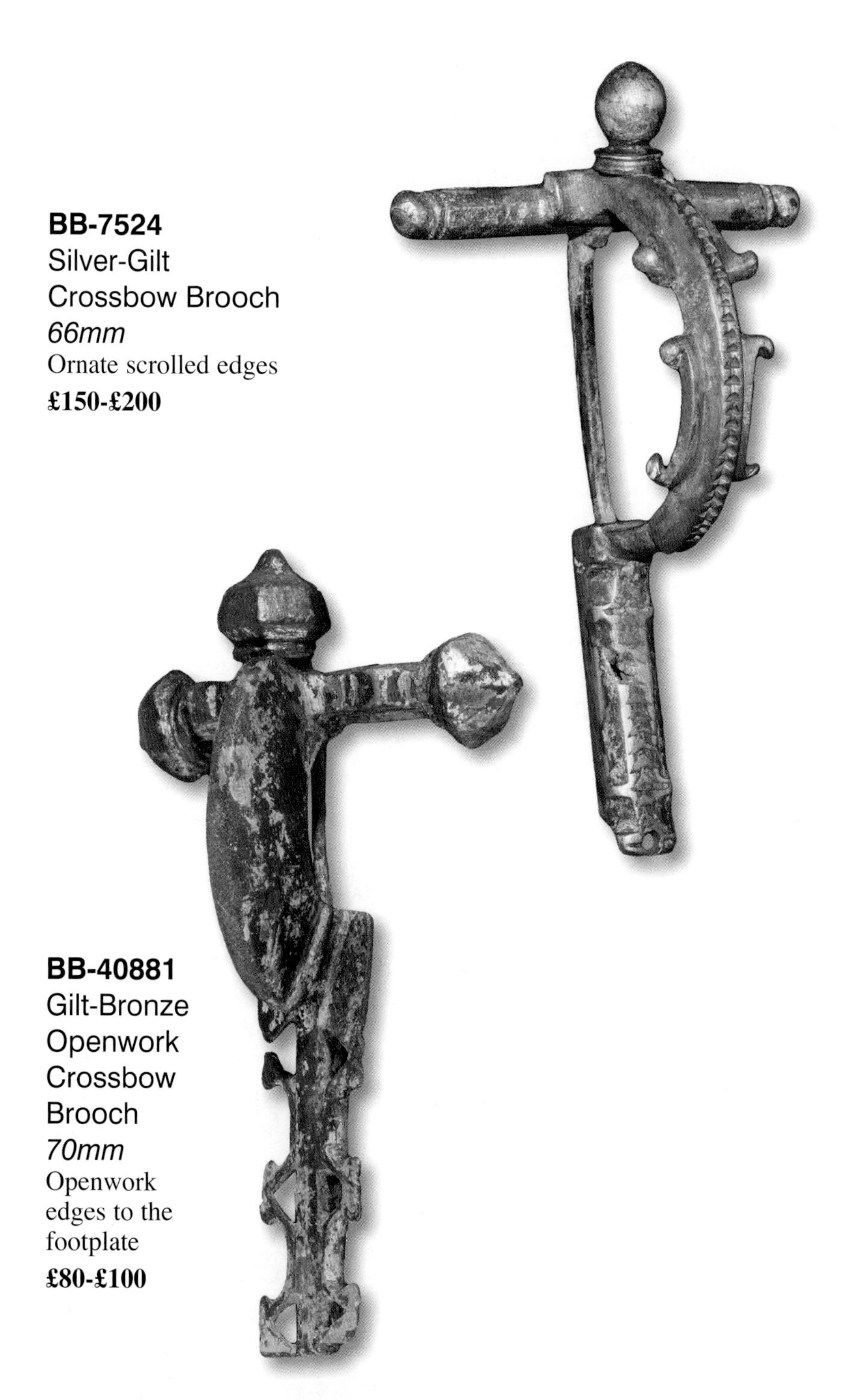

BB-7524
Silver-Gilt Crossbow Brooch
66mm
Ornate scrolled edges
£150-£200

BB-40881
Gilt-Bronze Openwork Crossbow Brooch
70mm
Openwork edges to the footplate
£80-£100

BB-8220
Gilt-Bronze
Crossbow Brooch
101mm
Onion-shaped knops, serrated edges on the footplate
£100-£150

BB-32186
Gilt-Bronze
Crossbow Brooch
74mm
Chamfered edges on the footplate
£100-£150

BB-7135
Gilt-Bronze Crossbow Brooch
85mm
Onion-shaped knops
£100-£150

BB-61917
Crossbow Brooch
86mm
Parcel-gilt
£80-£100

BB-1186
Crossbow Brooch
67mm
Parcel-gilt with chamfered footplate
£80-£120

BB-32163
Iron Bow Brooch
59mm
Parcel-gilt
£80-£100

BB-40886
Iron Bow Brooch
61mm
Silver inlay
£60-£80

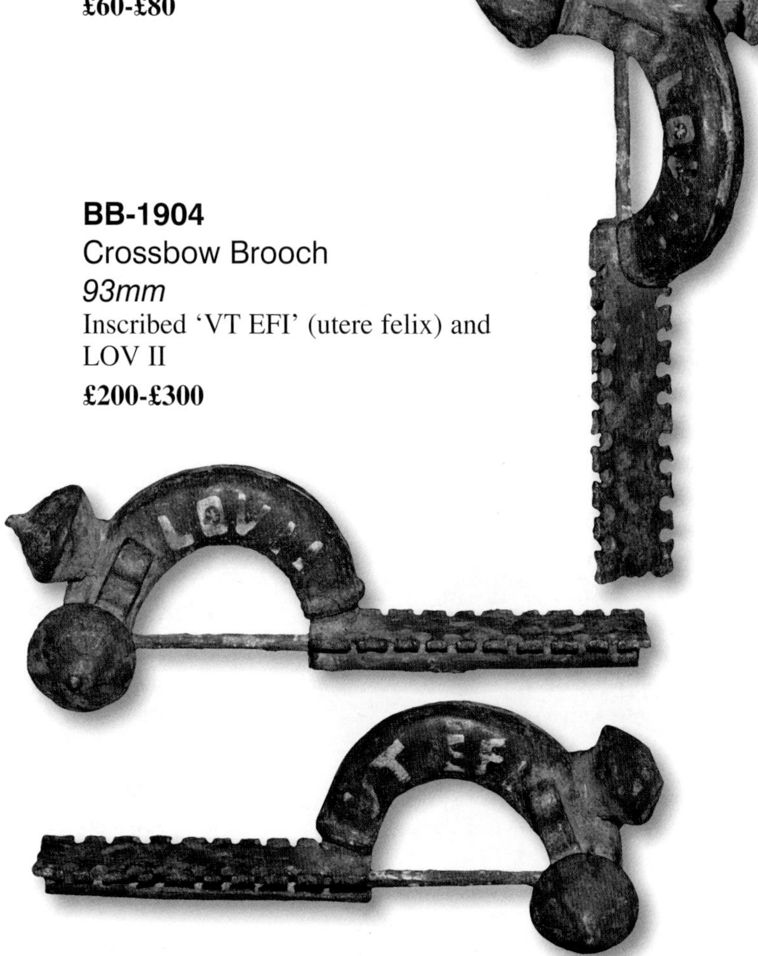

BB-1904
Crossbow Brooch
93mm
Inscribed ‘VT EFI’ (utere felix) and LOV II
£200-£300

BB-43422
Beaded Bow Brooch
54mm
Enamel panels, beast-head finials
£120-£180

BB-50520
Equal-Armed Bow Brooch
44mm
Triangular panels
£100-£150

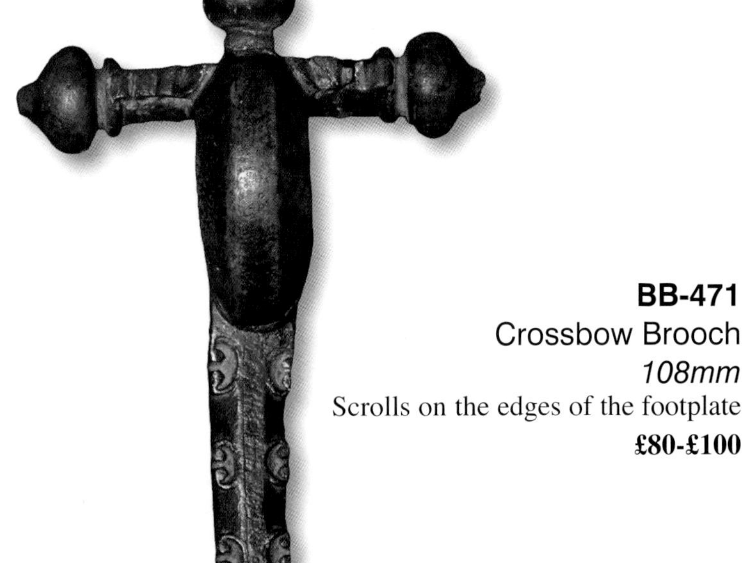

BB-471
Crossbow Brooch
108mm
Scrolls on the edges of the footplate
£80-£100

BB-10645
Crossbow Brooch
77mm
Granulation on the footplate
£100-150

BB-50483
Crossbow Brooch
115mm
Openwork detail on the footplate
£100-£150

BB-2160
Crossbow Brooch
150mm
Ring-and-dot details on the bow and footplate
£70-£90

BB-4332
Crossbow Brooch
85mm
Chamfered edges on the footplate
£80-£100

BB-60773
Crossbow Brooch
95mm
Onion-shaped knops with spikes
£80-100

BB-11269
Crossbow Brooch
88mm
Flat footplate with catchplate to the rear
£80-£100

BB-37292
Crossbow Brooch
92mm
Ring-and-dot motifs on the footplate
£80-£100

BB-14768
Crossbow Brooch
96mm
Early type with bulb knops
£50-£70

BB-52193
P-Shaped Bow Brooch
74mm
Punched detail on the bow and footplate
£50-£70

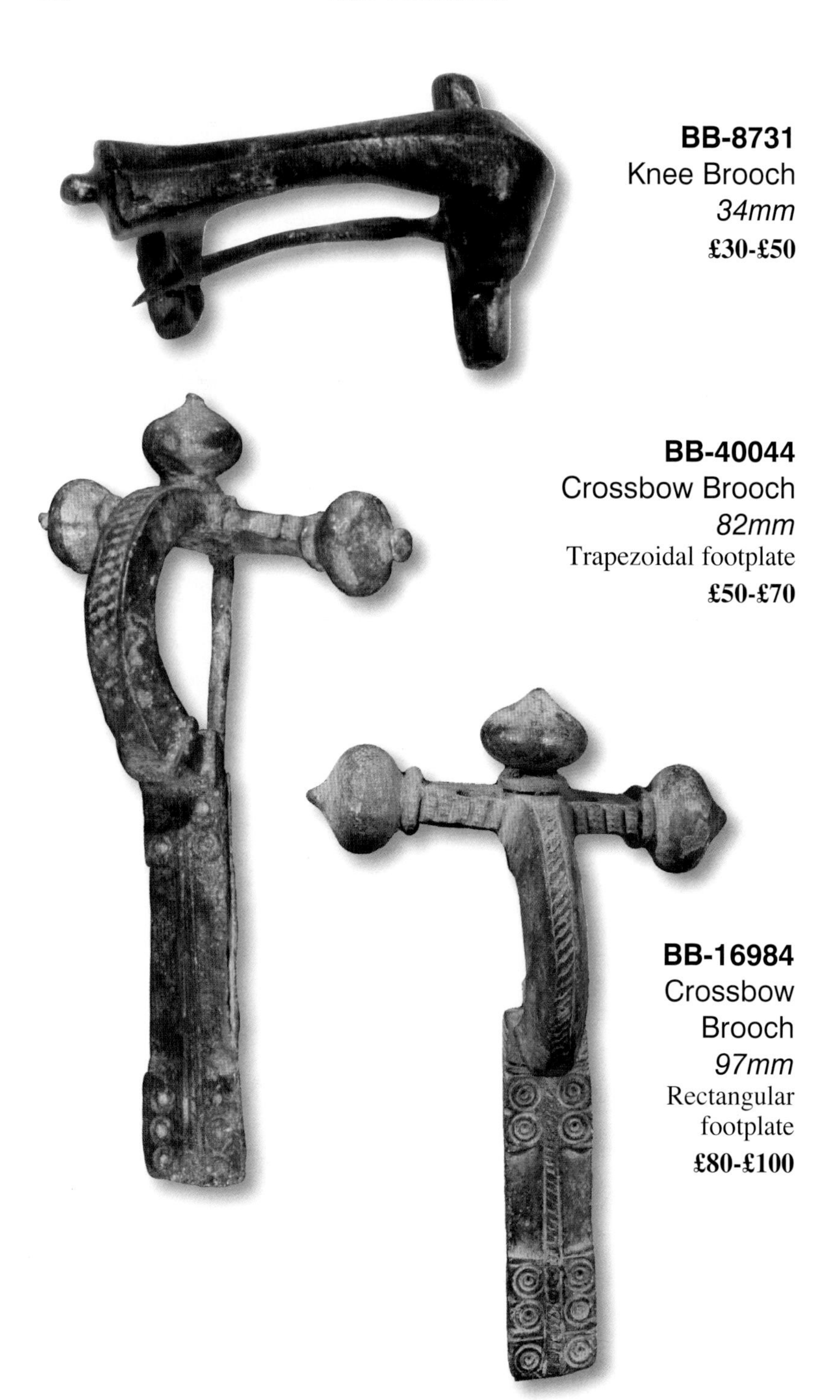

BB-8731
Knee Brooch
34mm
£30-£50

BB-40044
Crossbow Brooch
82mm
Trapezoidal footplate
£50-£70

BB-16984
Crossbow
Brooch
97mm
Rectangular
footplate
£80-£100

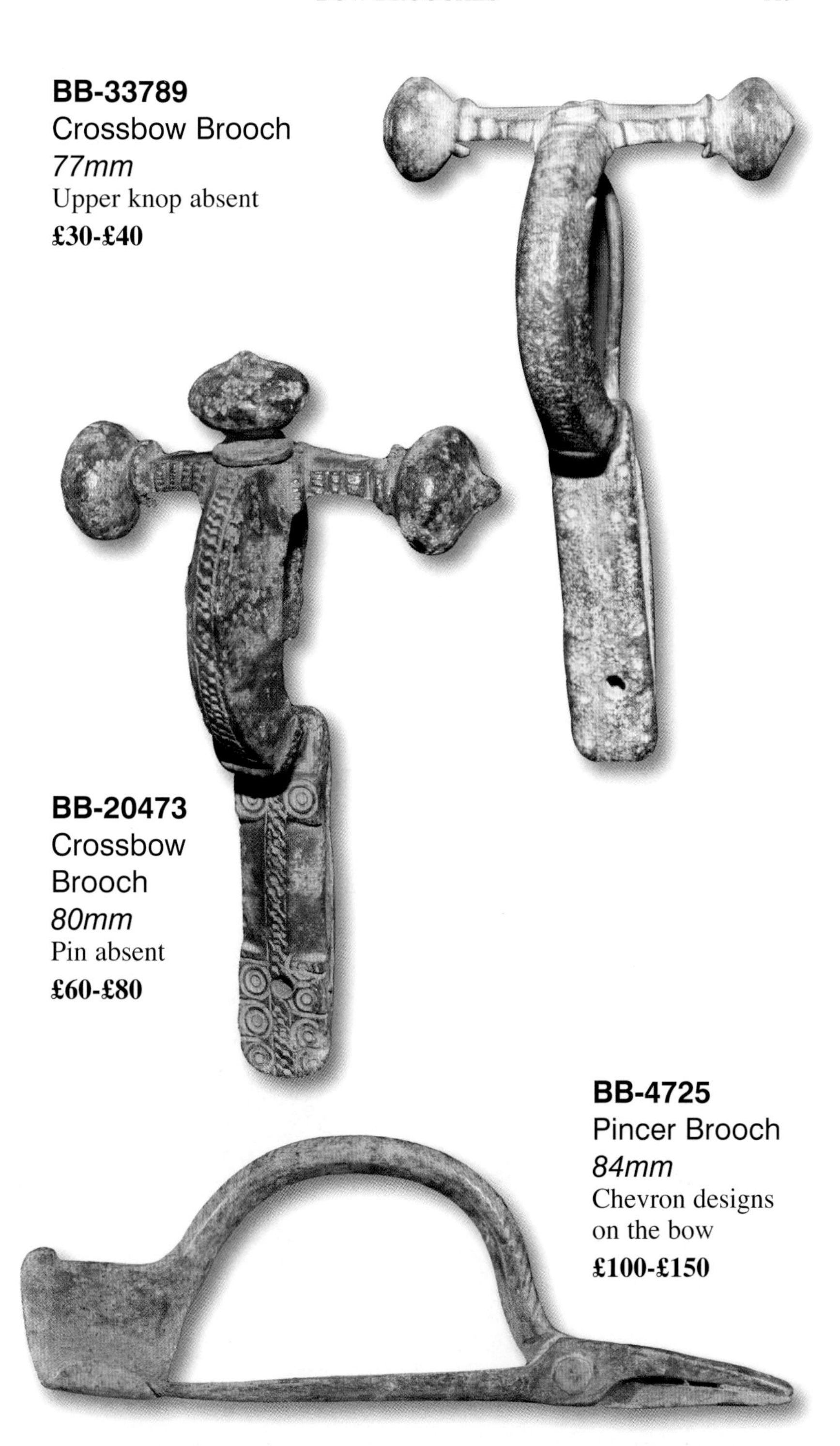

BB-33789
Crossbow Brooch
77mm
Upper knop absent
£30-£40

BB-20473
Crossbow Brooch
80mm
Pin absent
£60-£80

BB-4725
Pincer Brooch
84mm
Chevron designs on the bow
£100-£150

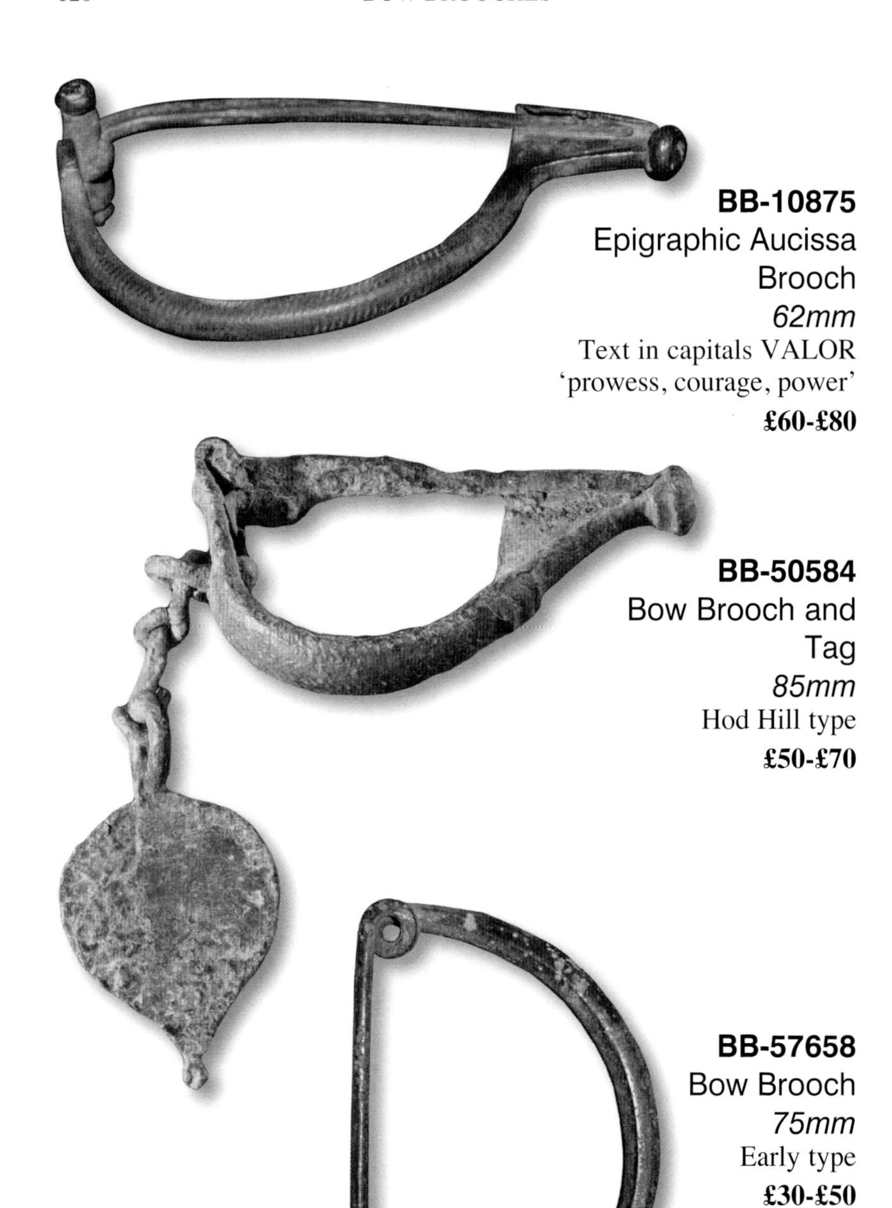

BB-10875
Epigraphic Aucissa Brooch
62mm
Text in capitals VALOR 'prowess, courage, power'
£60-£80

BB-50584
Bow Brooch and Tag
85mm
Hod Hill type
£50-£70

BB-57658
Bow Brooch
75mm
Early type
£30-£50

BB-26248
Enamelled Bow Brooch
42mm
Bow-and-fantail type, triangular enamelled footplate
£60-£80

BB-15116
Enamelled Bow Brooch
42mm
Lozenge-shaped bow
£40-£60

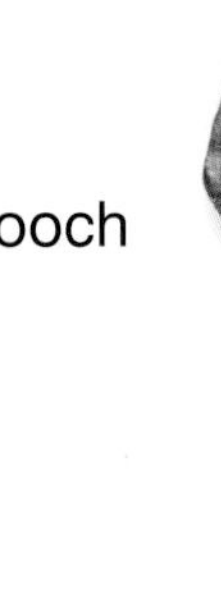

BB-10020
Enamelled Bow-and-Fantail Brooch
33mm
Triangular enamel panels
£40-£50

BB-62869
Enamelled Aucissa Brooch
28mm
Enamelled roundels to the bow
£30-£40

BB-50583
Bow Brooch
59mm
Aucissa-derivative type
£20-£30

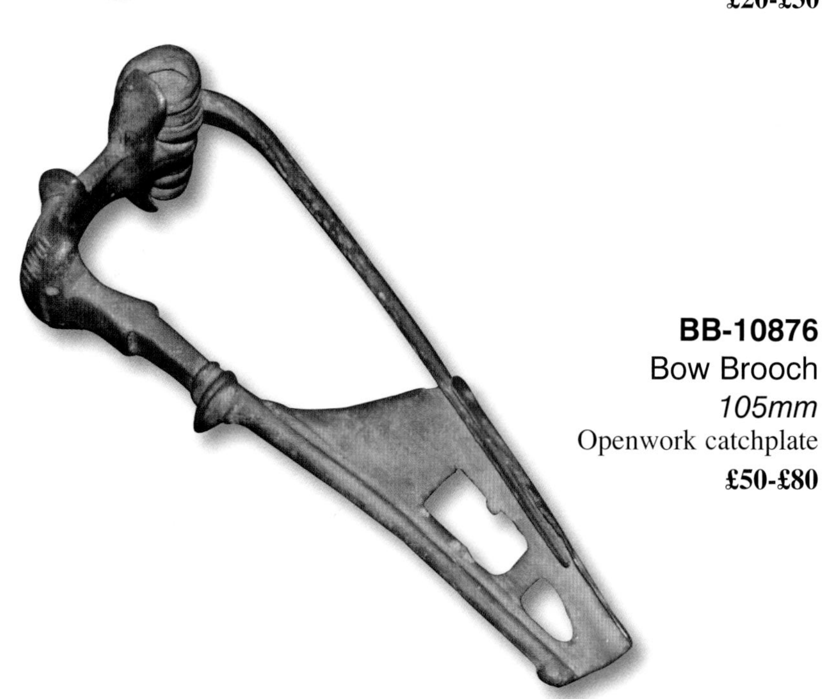

BB-10876
Bow Brooch
105mm
Openwork catchplate
£50-£80

BB-33786
Bow Brooch
63mm
Trumpet-derivative type
£20-£30

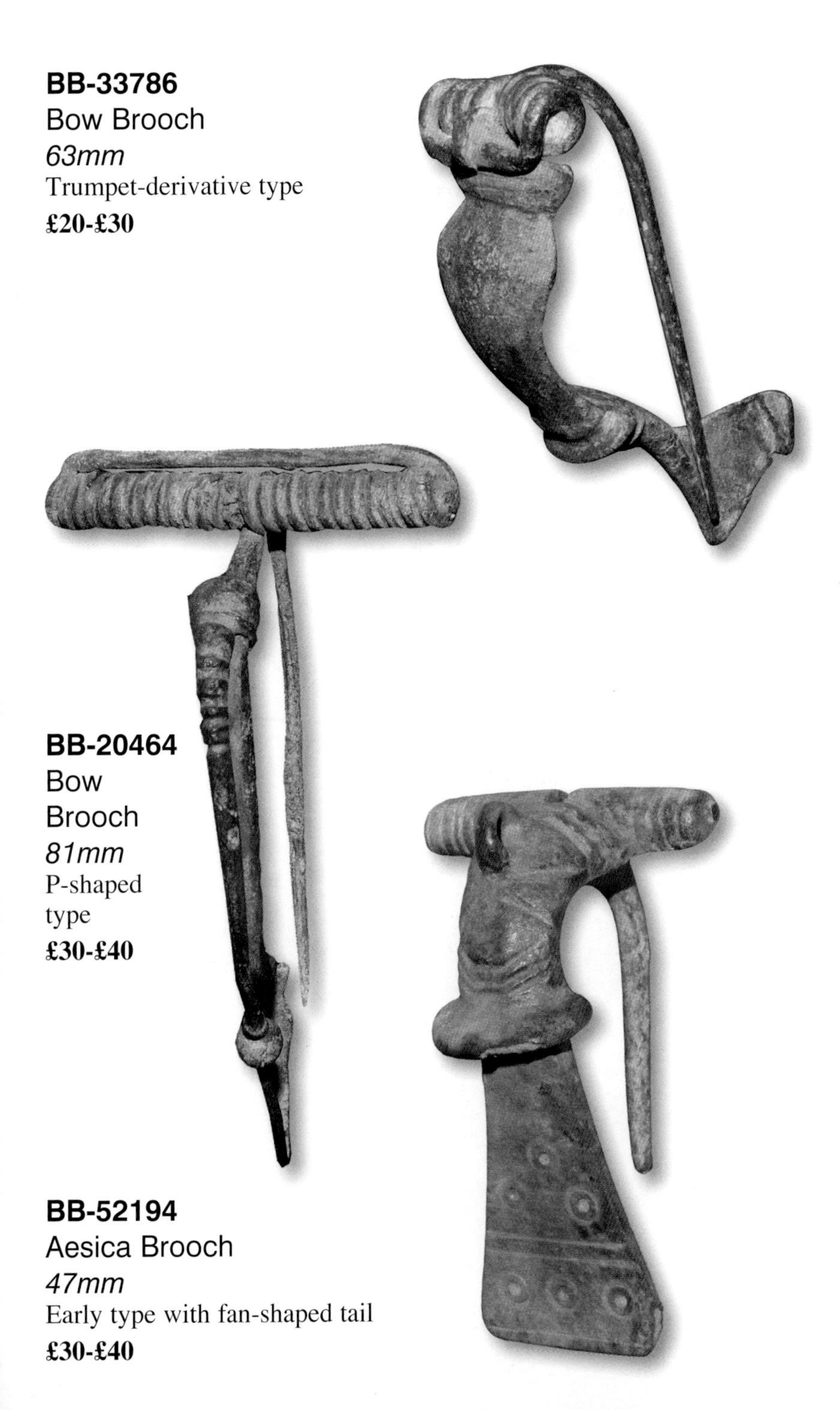

BB-20464
Bow
Brooch
81mm
P-shaped
type
£30-£40

BB-52194
Aesica Brooch
47mm
Early type with fan-shaped tail
£30-£40

BB-9949
Silver Trumpet Brooch
12mm
Punched detailing
£80-100

BB-4284
Silver Trumpet-Derivative Brooch
57mm
Punched detailing
£100-£150

BB-57737
Trumpet Brooch
35mm
Partly tinned
£40-£60

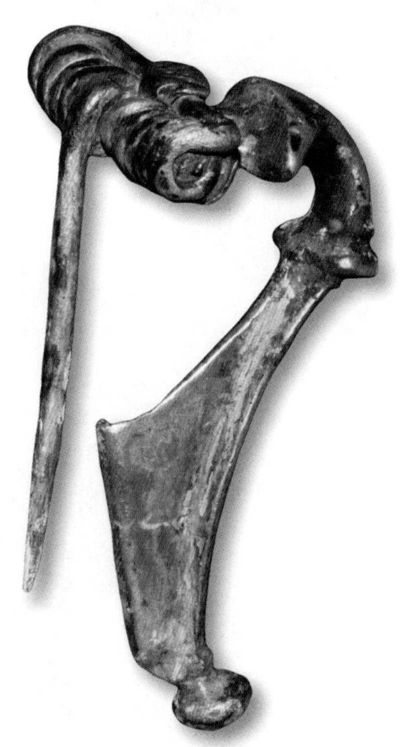

BB-60748
Silver Trumpet Brooch
50mm
Pelta-shaped headplate
£60-£80

PB-20326
Silver
Openwork
Brooch
32mm
La Tène style
£120-£180

PB-11959
Silver Parcel-Gilt Trumpets
Brooch
45mm
La Tène style
£300-£400

PB-1150
Silver-Gilt
Trumpet
Brooch Head
25mm
£150-£200

PB-62875
Openwork Trumpet Brooch
40mm
La Tène style
£30-£40

PB-25988
Silver
Trumpet
Whorl
Brooch
38mm
La Tène
style
£150-£200

PB-31341
Silver Trumpet-and-Leaves
Brooch
47mm
La Tène style
£150-£200

PB-23326
Silver Triskele Plate Brooch
29mm
La Tène style
£120-£180

PB-37299
Trumpet-Whorl Plate Brooch
47mm
La Tène style
£40-£60

PB-64660
Trumpet Whorl Plate Brooch
43mm
La Tène style
£60-£80

PB-64694
Openwork Plate Brooch
40mm
La Tène style
£40-£60

PB-64692
Openwork Brooch
53mm
La Tène style
£40-£60

PB-37300
Trumpet-Scroll Plate Brooch
33mm
La Tène style
£40-£60

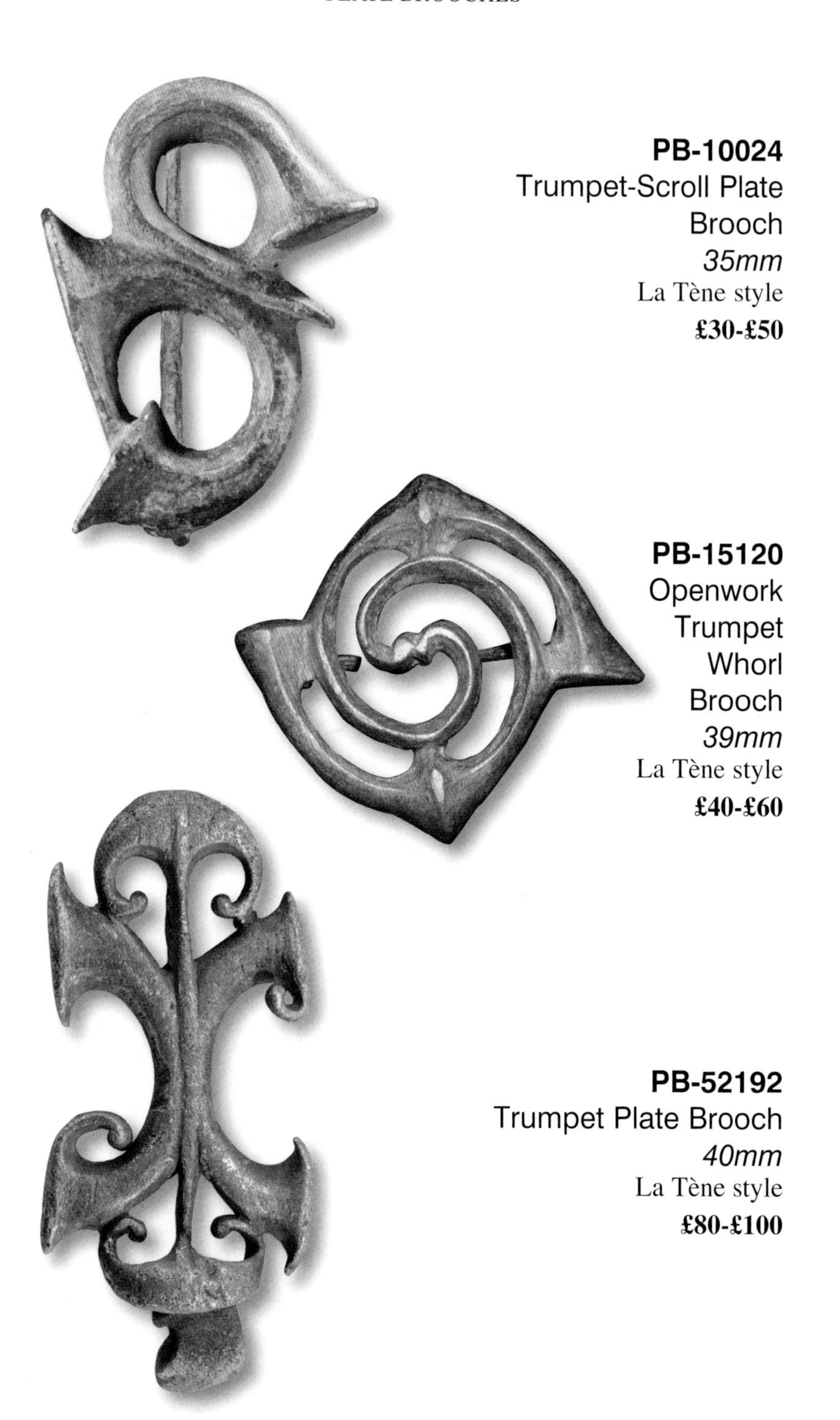

PB-10024
Trumpet-Scroll Plate Brooch
35mm
La Tène style
£30-£50

PB-15120
Openwork Trumpet Whorl Brooch
39mm
La Tène style
£40-£60

PB-52192
Trumpet Plate Brooch
40mm
La Tène style
£80-£100

PB-46475
Temple Plate Brooch
36mm
Arcade and pillars
£50-£70

PB-63020
Temple Plate Brooch
33mm
£50-£70

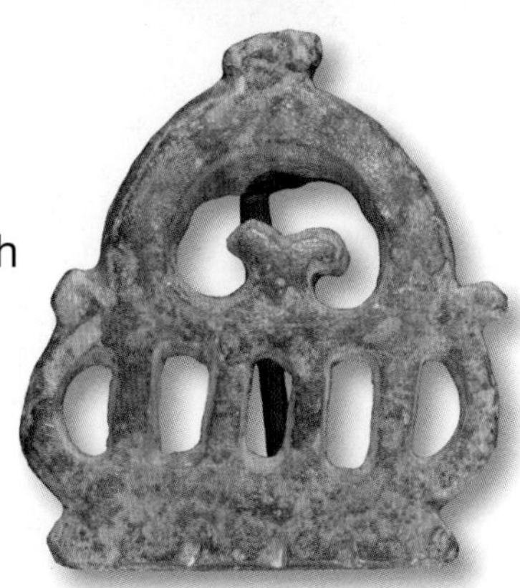

PB-42074
Openwork Plate Brooch
32mm
Temple type
£30-£40

PB-20229
Openwork
Plate Brooch
31mm
Temple type
£30-£40

PB-20471
Openwork
Plate Brooch
38mm
Temple type
£30-£40

PB-10022
Openwork Plate
Brooch
36mm
Temple type
£40-£60

PB-17100
Labrys Plate Brooch
41mm
£40-£60

PB-3401
Double Axe
Plate Brooch
33mm
Labrys type
£40-£60

PB-64690
Double
Axe Plate
Brooch
35mm
Labrys type
£40-£60

PB-19634
Silver Galley Plate Brooch
24mm
With three crewmen
£200-£300

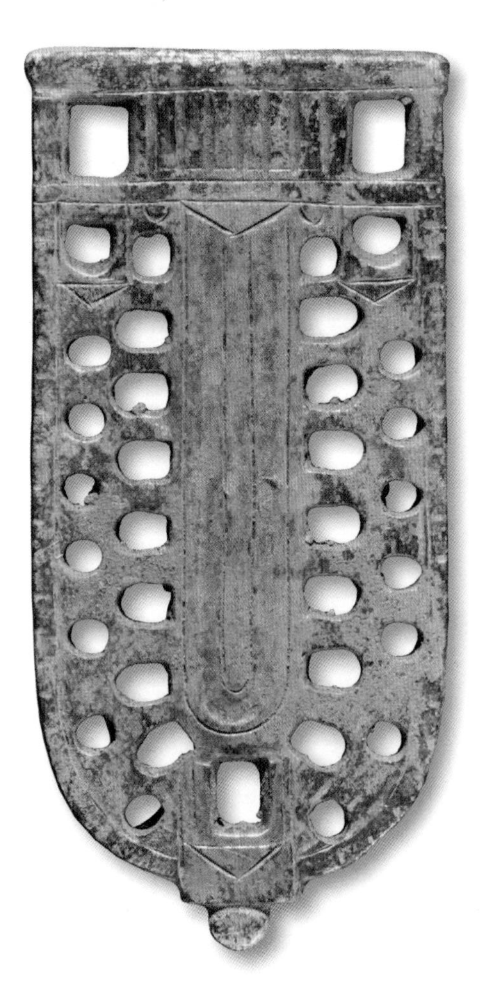

PB-47498
Circus Plate Brooch
60mm
Plan of a circus race-track
£400-£600

PB-7127
Silver Openwork
Amphora Brooch
31mm
Amphora and tendrils
£200-£300

PB-62874
Flask Brooch
36mm
Amphora and
tendrils
£40-£60

PB-8209
Plate Brooch
34mm
Double amphora
with mask
£40-£60

PB-24254
Silver-Gilt Brooch
29mm
With mask of Eros
£300-£400

PB-10056
Plate Brooch
38mm
Two putti in a frame
£100-£150

PB-63064
ROMA Plate Brooch
43mm
Openwork monogram of 'ROMA'
£70-£90

70272
Silver ROMA Plate Brooch
32mm
Monogram with the 'O' forming the outer border
£100-£150

PB-54353
Openwork Plate Brooch
36mm
Swastika within a ring
£40-£60

PB-60448
Openwork Plate Brooch
39mm
Scrolls and leaves
£50-£70

PB-50586
Openwork Plate Brooch
29mm
Geometric type
£40-£60

PB-62872
Openwork Plate Brooch
38mm
Scrolled tendrils type
£40-£60

PB-20477
Openwork Plate Brooch
30mm
Geometric type
£30-£40

PB-62871
Tinned Openwork
Plate Brooch
33mm
Volute scrolls type
£30-£40

PB-42073
Sun Wheel Plate
Brooch
35mm
Radiating arcs and spokes
£40-£60

PB-17098
Openwork Plate
Brooch
38mm
Radiating trumpets type
£40-£60

PB-15115
Openwork Wheel Brooch
30mm
Radiating arcs type
£40-£60

PB-15121
Openwork Plate Brooch
35mm
Radiating trumpets type
£30-£40

PB-20479
Openwork Plate Brooch
41mm
Tendrils and scrolls type
£40-£60

PB-26363
Openwork Plate Brooch
34mm
Lozenge type
£60-£80

PB-18541
Openwork Plate Brooch
38mm
Leaves and scrolls type
£30-£40

PB-18545
Openwork Plate Brooch
46mm
Vineleaves type
£30-£50

PB-60450
Swastika Plate Brooch
32mm
Swastika type
£30-£50

PB-19625
Swastika Plate Brooch
32mm
Lightning bolts
£50-£70

PB-18542
Swastika Plate Brooch
29mm
£30-£50

PB-15114
Swastika Plate Brooch
30mm
£30-£50

PB-11946
Swastika Plate Brooch
26mm
£30-£50

PB-20470
Serpents Plate Brooch
28mm
Looped serpents with raised heads
£30-£40

PB-54716
Tinned Plate Brooch
38mm
With bone discs
£100-£150

PB-17099
Enamelled Plate Brooch
35mm
With bone discs
£50-£70

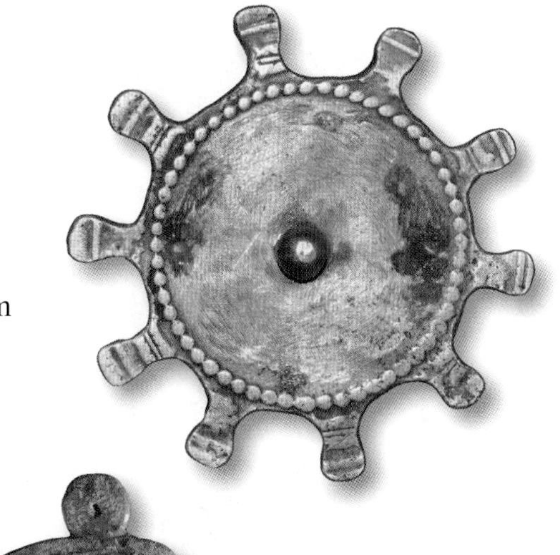

PB-23229
Silver Sun-Wheel Brooch
38mm
Radiating pegs to the rim
£120-£180

PB-51780
Plate Brooch
59mm
Disc and radiating lobes
£50-£70

PB-64695
Tinned Plate Brooch
43mm
Disc and tendrils beneath
£40-£60

PB-46477
Plate Brooch
37mm
Disc and lobes type
£40-£60

PB-20476
Plate Brooch
30mm
Expanding arm
cross type
£30-£40

PB-65299
Plate
Brooch
48mm
Square type
with scrolls
£80-£100

PB-52186
Plate Brooch
47mm
Dense mesh of tendrils
£50-£70

PB-60446
Plate Brooch
64mm
Shield-shaped type
£50-£70

PB-20466
Plate Brooch
39mm
Lantern type
£20-£30

PB-20474
Plate Brooch
49mm
Lozenge type
£30-£40

PB-57735
Silver Plate Brooch
40mm
Lozenge type
£80-£100

PB-20472
Plate Brooch
46mm
Lozenge type
£20-£30

PB-28354
Gilt-Bronze
Plate Brooch
26mm
Disc type with
chamfered rim
£40-£60

PB-42099
Gilt-Bronze
Tutulus Brooch
22mm
Central spike
£40-£60

PB-15119
Enamelled Disc
Brooch
27mm
Segmented body
£30-£40

PB-26241
Enamelled Disc Brooch
23mm
Segmented body
£40-£60

PB-18121
Enamelled Plate Brooch
26mm
Segmented body
£60-£80

PB-19624
Enamelled Plate Brooch
31mm
Segmented body
£80-£100

PB-40012
Enamelled Wheel Brooch
20mm
Hub and spokes type
£50-£70

PB-42080
Millefiori Disc Brooch
23mm
Hub and spokes type
£50-£70

PB-40045
Umbonate Disc Brooch
35mm
Domed central section
£30-£40

PB-28589
Gilt-Bronze Enamelled
Equal-Arm Brooch
49mm
Disc and lugs
£100-£150

PB-38751
Enamelled Wheel
Brooch
36mm
Radiating lugs
£100-£150

PB-62099
Enamelled
Knopped Plate
Brooch
23mm
Radiating knops
£60-£80

PB-11670
Enamelled Annular Brooch
38mm
Heart-shaped plaques
£100-£150

PB-8728
Enamelled Disc Brooch
26mm
£70-£90

PB-28261
Enamelled Disc Brooch
36mm
Radiating knops
£30-£50

PB-54101
Enamelled Disc Brooch
34mm
Radiating knops
£50-£70

PB-51507
Enamelled Plate Brooch
39mm
Segmented wheel type
£50-£70

PB-18540
Enamelled Plate Brooch
35mm
Four radiating lobes
£30-£50

PB-10019
Enamelled Plate Brooch
34mm
Segmented wheel type
£30-£40

PB-2619
Enamelled Disc Brooch
28mm
Segmented wheel type
£100-£150

PB-19301
Disc Brooch
20mm
Millefiori panel
From £300

PB-34358
Disc Brooch
31mm
Millefiori panel
£120-£180

PB-15077
Epigraphic Disc Brooch
53mm
Inscribed MAG [..]M NGNIS (magnum ignis 'great fire'?)
£100-£150

PB-20465
Enamelled Plate Brooch
27mm
Enamelled panel
£30-£40

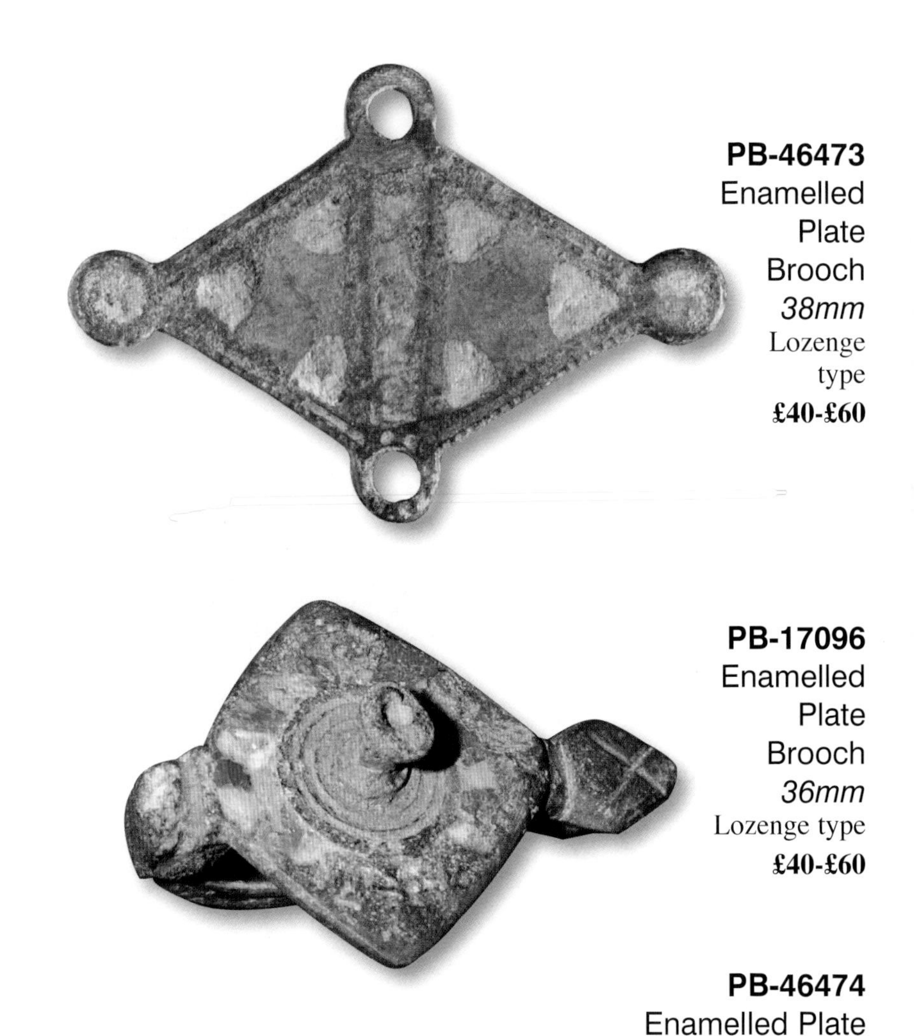

PB-46473
Enamelled Plate Brooch
38mm
Lozenge type
£40-£60

PB-17096
Enamelled Plate Brooch
36mm
Lozenge type
£40-£60

PB-46474
Enamelled Plate Brooch
53mm
Lozenge type
£40-£60

PB-20468
Enamelled Plate Brooch
26mm
Lozenge type
£30-£50

PB-20475
Enamelled Plate Brooch
30mm
Lozenge type
£30-£40

PB-59399
Enamelled and Tinned Plate Brooch
37mm
Lozenge type with arms
£40-£60

PB-51506
Enamelled
Plate Brooch
43mm
Ring of discs with
radiating arms
£40-£60

PB-23226
Silver Enamelled
Lozenge Brooch
34mm
Lozenge type
£120-£180

PB-30492
Enamelled Plate Brooch
57mm
Disc with crescents
£150-£200

PB-51505
Enamelled Plate Brooch
41mm
Square grid with enamel
£40-£60

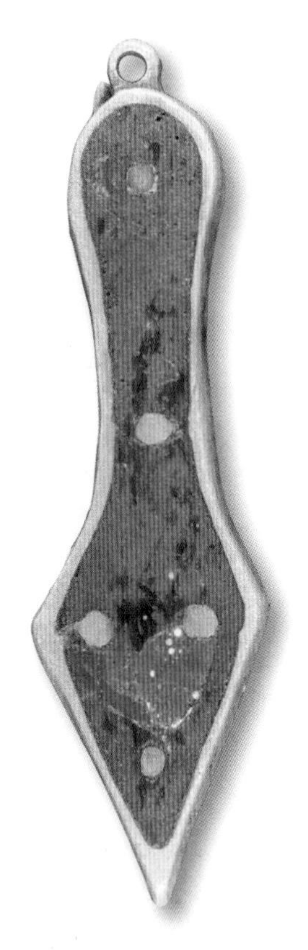

PB-11850
Silver Enamelled
Plate Brooch
38mm
Sandal type with studs
From £300

PB-30425
Enamelled Lunar
Deity Brooch
33mm
Facing bust with
enamel fill
£100-£150

PB-53221
Enamelled Plate Brooch
48mm
Crescent type
£50-£70

PB-37297
Crescent Plate Brooch
32mm
Enamelled roundel
£30-£50

PB-35829
Enamelled Crescent-Armed Brooch
45mm
Disc with crescents
£120-£180

PB-52111
Enamelled Amphora Brooch
46mm
Openwork amphora shape
£300-£400

PB-31207
Enamelled Plate Brooch
43mm
Volute scrolled type
£120-£180

PB-47502
Amphora Plate Brooch
40mm
Amphora with panels
£100-£150

PB-26479
Gladiator Brooch
45mm
Standing Murmillo with sword and shield
£200-£300

PB-54744
Magister Militium Figural Brooch
41mm
Cloaked military figure
£150-£200

PB-57706
Gladiator Brooch
40mm
Secutor with drawn sword
£150-£200

PB-34547
Gladiator
Brooch
35mm
Secutor with
drawn sword
£100-£150

PB-46597
Silver Parade
Brooch Pair
82-87mm
Lozenges joined by a
susbstantial chain
From £1,000

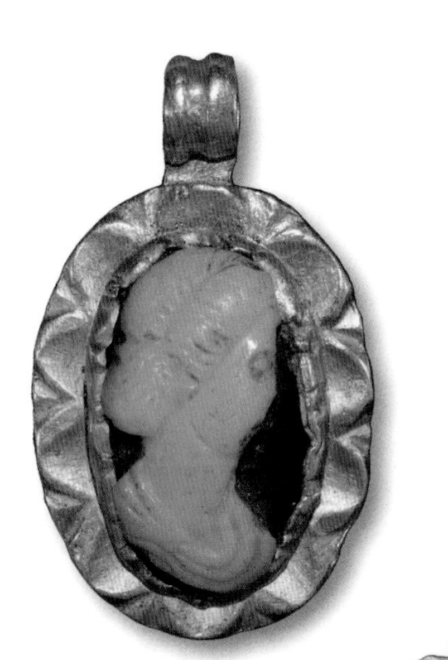

PN-7382
Gold Pendant
27mm
Faustina Junior cameo
£400-£600

PN-46584
Gold
Pendant
26mm
Eros cameo
£400-£600

PN-65328
Gold Pendant
27mm
Garnet cabochon
£300-£400

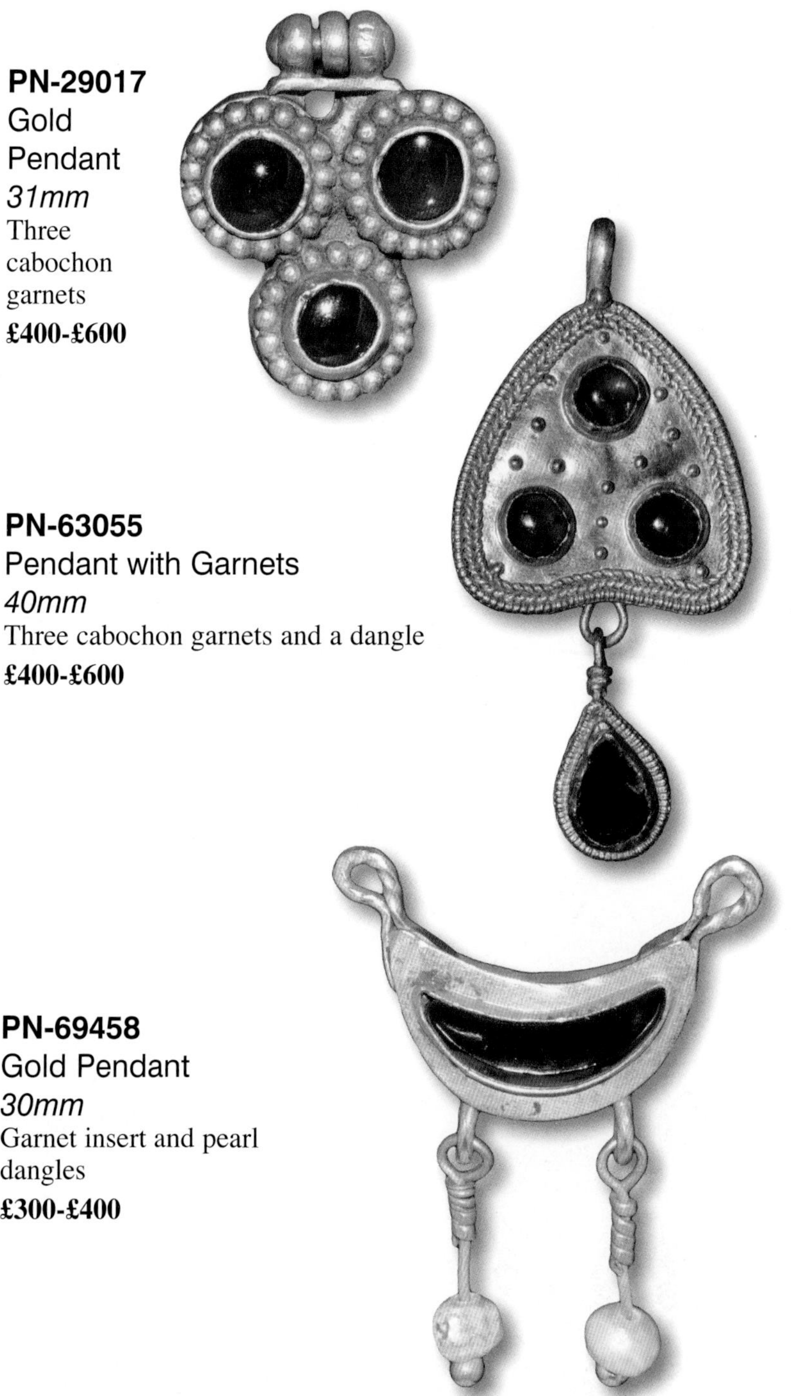

PN-29017
Gold
Pendant
31mm
Three
cabochon
garnets
£400-£600

PN-63055
Pendant with Garnets
40mm
Three cabochon garnets and a dangle
£400-£600

PN-69458
Gold Pendant
30mm
Garnet insert and pearl
dangles
£300-£400

PN-39052
Gold Pendant
18mm
Teardrop garnet
£200-£300

PN-43761
Gold Lozenge Pendant
20mm
Carnelian cabochon
£100-£150

PN-14860
Gold Pendant
20mm
Amethyst drop
£120-£180

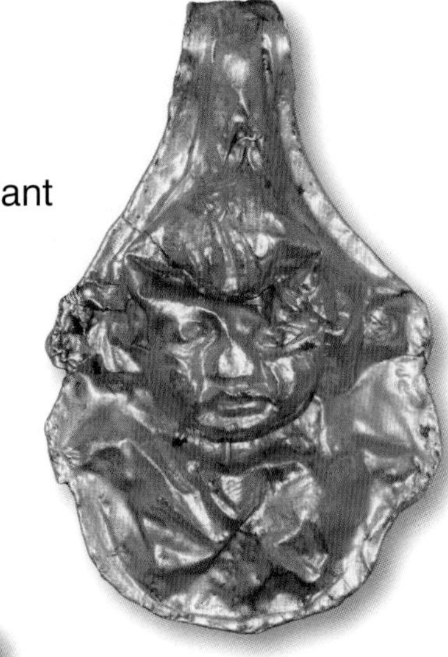

PN-12933
Gold Repoussé Figural Pendant
37mm
Facing mask
£200-£300

PN-41107
Gold Fortuna
Pendant
18mm
Bracteate type
£200-£300

PN-59582
Gold Pendant with Bird
18mm
Bird within a ropework border
£150-£200

PN-51361
Gold Repoussé Pendant
27mm
Rosette type
£100-£150

PN-1968
Filigree
Gold
Pendant
20mm
Miniature
pyxis type
£120-£180

PN-66157
Gold Hercules Club Pendant
37mm
Filigree detailing
£200-£300

PN-16444
Gold Axe Pendant
29mm
Granule detailing
£150-£200

PN-29004
Gold Tintinnabulum Crescent Pendant
53mm
Suspension loops to the edge
£200-£300

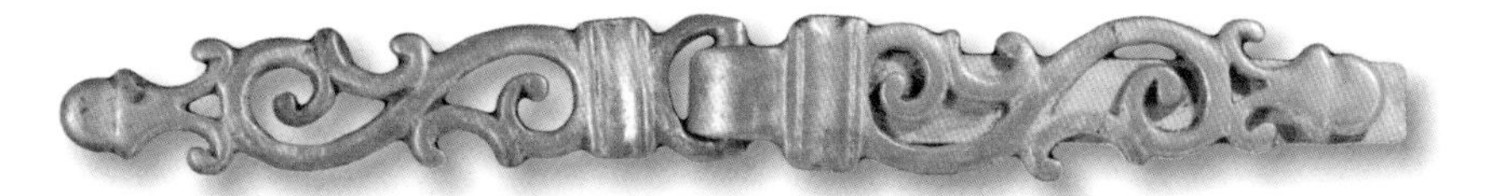

PN-11266
Silver Hinged Pendant
120mm
Elaborate scrollwork
£200-£300

PN-34555
Silver Pendant
44mm
Vineleaf type
£80-£100

PN-10937
Silver Dolphin Pendant
24mm
Profile image on a plaque
£100-£150

PN-1864
Pelta-Shaped Pendant
36mm
Inset scene with a horse and a winged figure
£120-£180

PN-2225
Silver Cupids Pendant
13mm
Putti with a vase
£70-£90

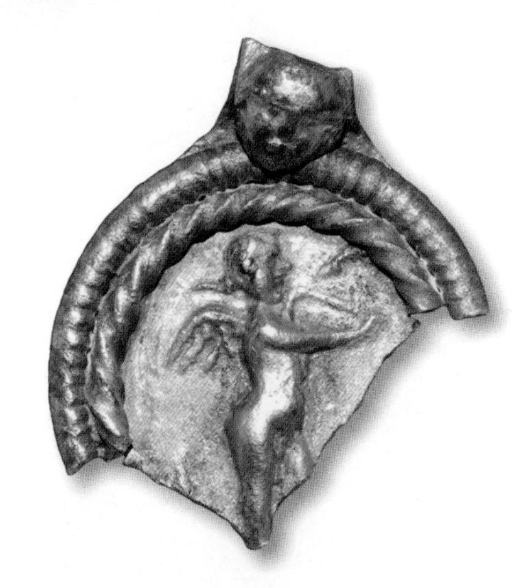

PN-31348
Silver Pendant
21mm
Cupid and mask
£60-£80

PN-66170
Pendant
48mm
Facing
Medusa bust
£100-£150

PN-20515
Female Bust Pendant
30mm
Female head and collar
£80-£100

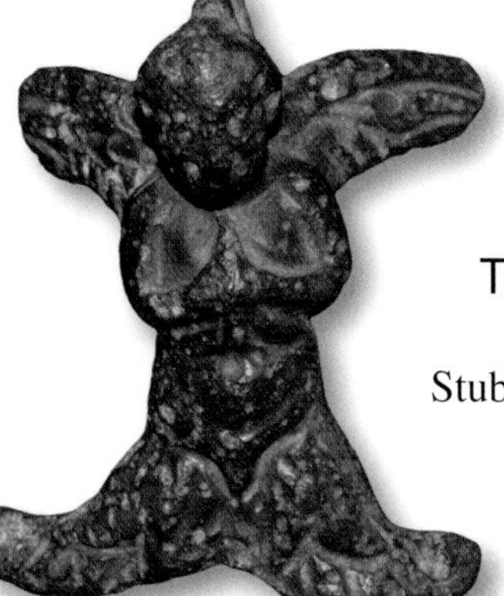

PN-2061
Triton Pendant
35mm
Stub wings and fish-tail feet
£60-£80

PN-8489
Female Bust Pendant
40mm
Facing mask with dressed hair
£40-£60

PN-1876
Silver
Mouse
Pendant
23mm
Eating a piece of food
£150-£200

PN-14797
Frog Amuletic
Pendant
45mm
Pierced lug
between the
back legs for
suspension
£50-£70

PN-69641
Military Horse
Harness Pendant
90mm
Ring-and-dot motifs
£100-£140

PN-30451
Gold Pendant
16mm
Winged phallus
From £400

PN-42437
Gold Pendant
28mm
Winged phallus
£300-£400

PN-3675
Gold Pendant
19mm
Phallus
£100-£150

PN-23468
Gold Pendant
19mm
Phallus
£100-£150

PN-45981
Gold Pendant
33mm
Phallus
From £500

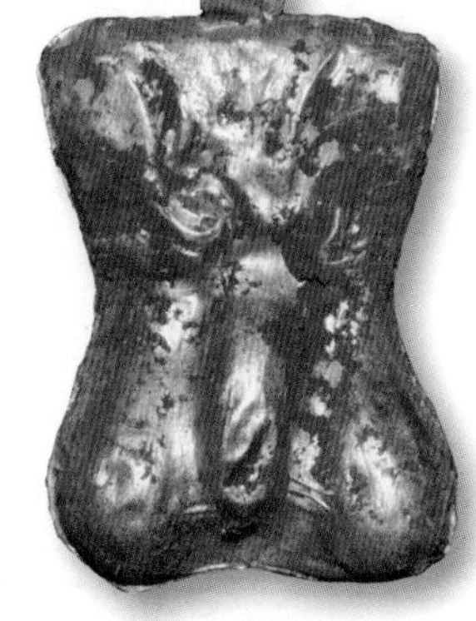

PN-9038
Gold Pendant
21mm
Male genitals
£200-£300

PN-64681
Silver Pendant
22mm
Winged phallus type
£120-£180

PN-23096
Silver Pendant
25mm
Phallus
£80-£100

PN-69477
Lunate Pendant with Phallus
46mm
Crescent pendant with separate model phallus
£80-£100

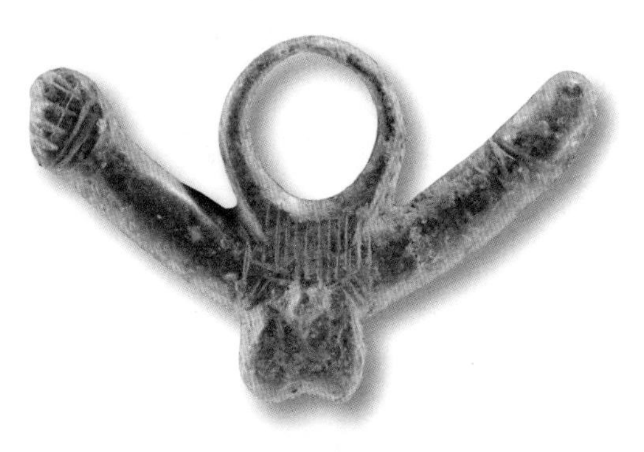

PN-8213
Phallic Pendant
66mm
Two phalloi and genitals
£100-£150

PN-20734
Phallic Bull Pendant
58mm
Bull and genitals
£120-£180

PN-3769
Phallic Pendant
72mm
Loops for suspension of amulets
£100-£150

PN-31123
Pendant
57mm
Phalloi and fist
£80-£100

PN-60863
Pendant
75mm
Phalloi and fist
£80-£100

PN-11752
Phallic Pendant
43mm
Phalloi and fist
£60-£80

PN-4655
Phallic Pendant
75mm
Phalloi and fist
£120-£180

PN-5399
Phallic Pendant
90mm
Phalloi and fist
£100-£150

PN-4654
Phallic Pendant
64mm
Phalloi and fist with loops
£100-£150

PN-1823
Phallus Pendant
62mm
Phalloi and fist
£80-£100

PN-20046
Double Phallic Pendant
56mm
Phalloi with loops
£80-£100

PN-7344
Phallic Pendant
37mm
Phalloi and genitals
£40-£60

PN-57679
Phallic Pendant
60mm
Phalloi and fist
£40-£60

PN-11019
Phallic Pendant
88mm
Phalloi and fist
£120-£180

PN-19643
Phallic Pendant
47mm
Crescents with phallus beneath
£80-£100

PN-4401
Phallic
Pendant
42mm
Male genitals
£40-£60

PN-38983
Phallic Pendant
29mm
Male genitals
£40-£60

PN-6757
Phallic Pendant
57mm
Male genitals
£30-£40

PN-11754
Phallic Pendant
46mm
Phallus with loop
£50-£70

PN-11755
Phallic Pendant
40mm
Phallus with loop
£50-£70

PN-11751
Phallic Pendant
44mm
Phallus with loop
£40-£60

PN-64993
Phallic Pendant
31mm
Phallus with loop
£30-£40

PN-11406
Phallic Pendant
45mm
Phallus with loop
£30-£40

PN-11753
Phallic Pendant
38mm
Phallus with loop
£30-£40

PN-11756
Phallic Pendant
35mm
Phallus with loop
£30-£40

PN-11757
Phallic Pendant
40mm
Phallus with loop
£30-£40

PN-11758
Phallic Pendant
37mm
Phallus with loop
£30-£40

PN-34567
Phallic Pendant
80mm
Phallus with loop
£30-£40

PN-7091
Phallic Pendant
50mm
Phallus with loop
£40-£60

PN-46468
Phallic Pendant
52mm
Phallus with loop
£60-£80

PN-56673
Phallic Pendant
62mm
Phallus with loop
£80-£100

PN-59285
Phallic Pendant
29mm
Phallus with loop
£30-£40

PN-59286
Phallic Pendant
29mm
Phallus with loop
£30-£40

PN-61904
Phallic Pendant
24mm
Phallus with loop
£30-£40

PN-64991
Phallic Pendant
34mm
Phallus with loop
£40-£60

PN-38919
Tintinnabulum
Pendant
82mm
Phalloi
£300-£400

PN-29099
Herm
Pendant
66mm
Male head and
genitals
£100-£150

PN-50510
Phallic Grotesque
Pendant
58mm
Phallus with grotesque
face above
£200-£300

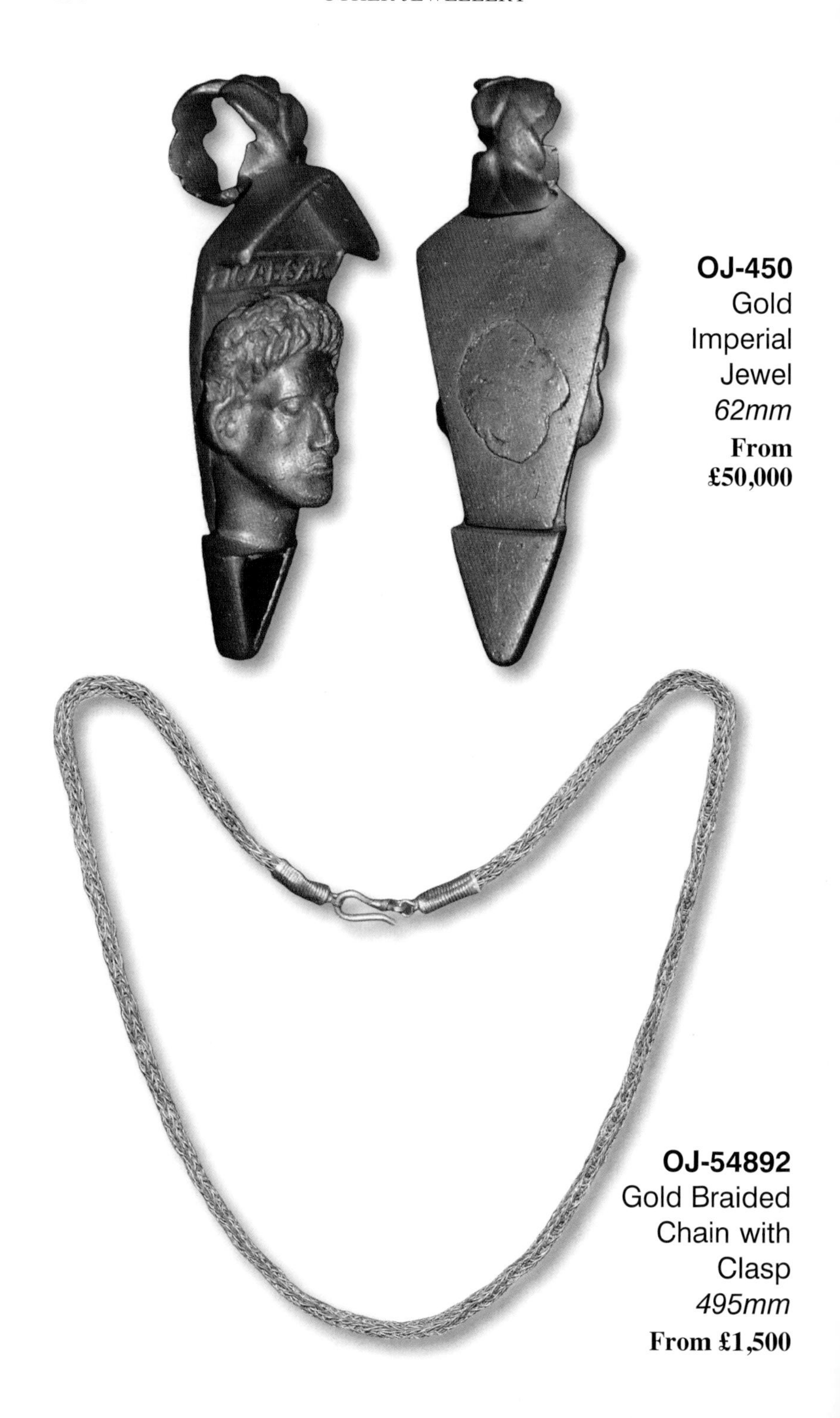

OJ-450
Gold Imperial Jewel
62mm
From £50,000

OJ-54892
Gold Braided Chain with Clasp
495mm
From £1,500

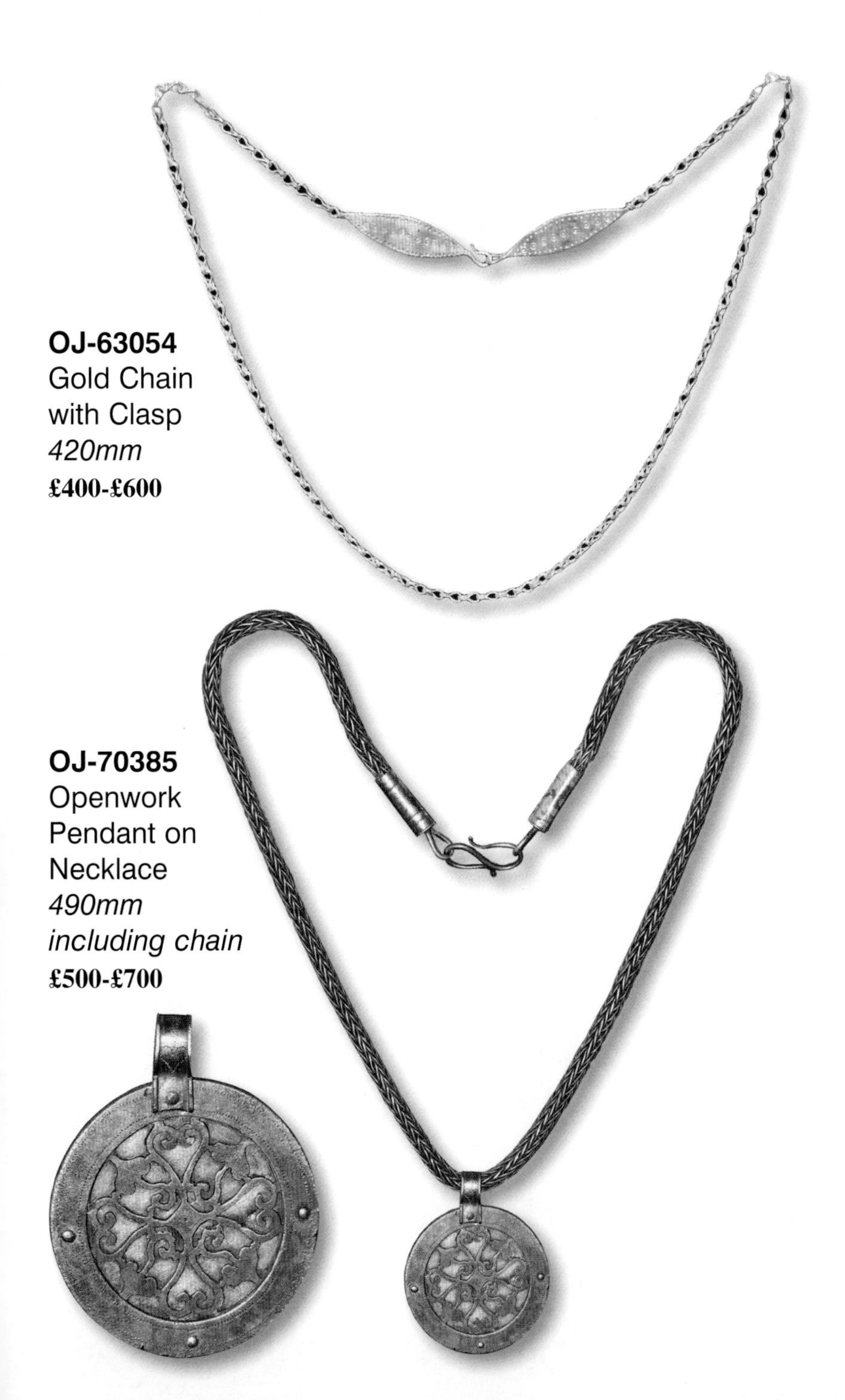

OJ-63054
Gold Chain
with Clasp
420mm
£400-£600

OJ-70385
Openwork
Pendant on
Necklace
490mm
including chain
£500-£700

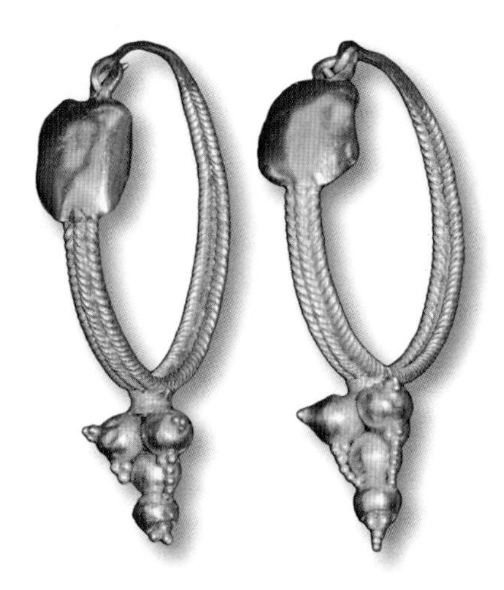

OJ-69460
Gold Earrings with
Filigree Pyramids
40mm
£400-£600

OJ-69479
Gold Earrings
with Pearls
34mm
£400-£600

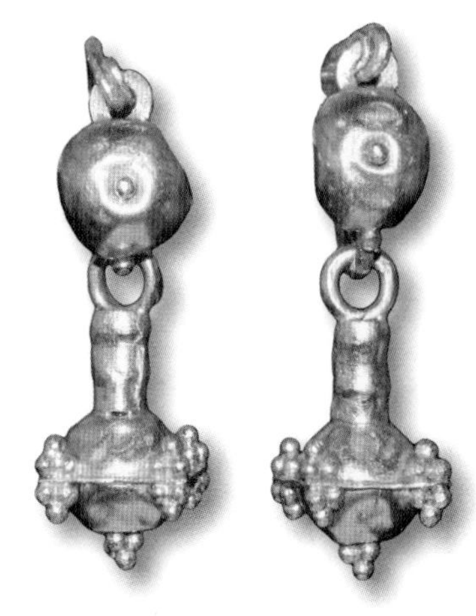

OJ-69755
Filigree Gold Earrings
28mm
£400-£600

OJ-69482
Gold Earrings
42mm
£400-£600

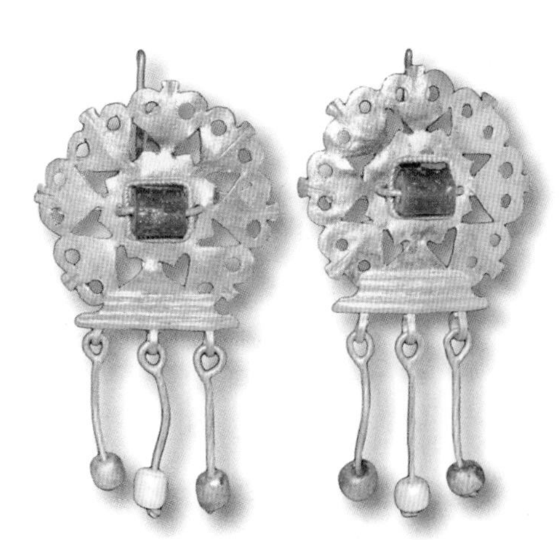

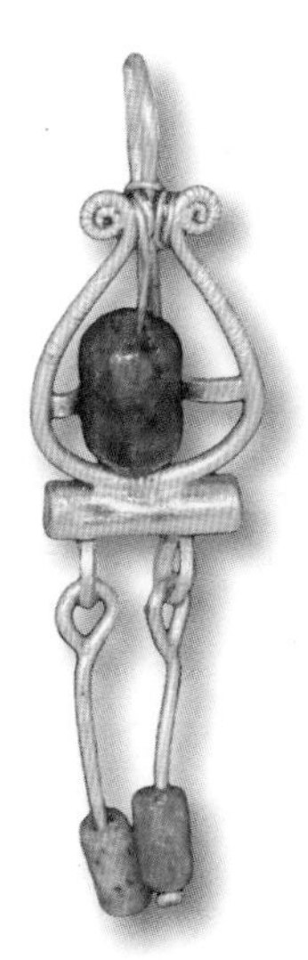

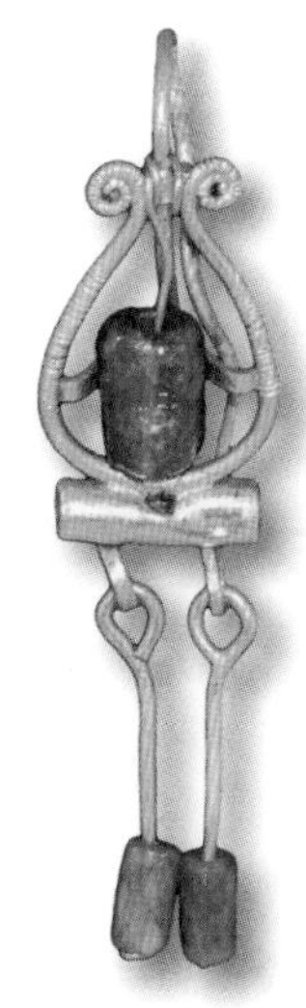

OJ-69786
Gold Earrings
with Drops
44mm
£400-£600

OJ-69754
Gold and Green
Glass Cabochon
Earrings
29mm
£300-£400

OJ-3322
Gold Hercules Club Earrings
48mm
£400-£600

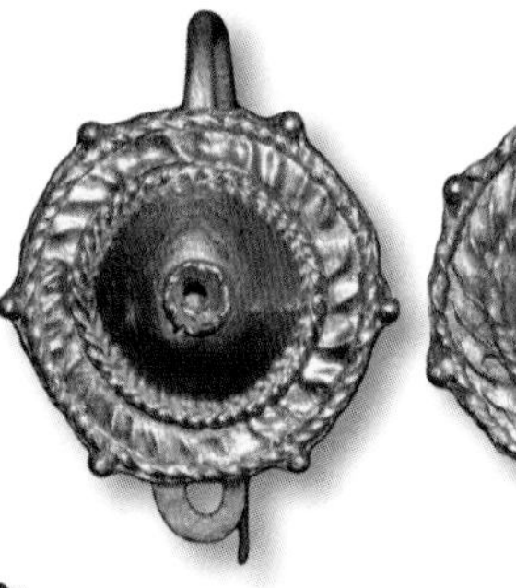

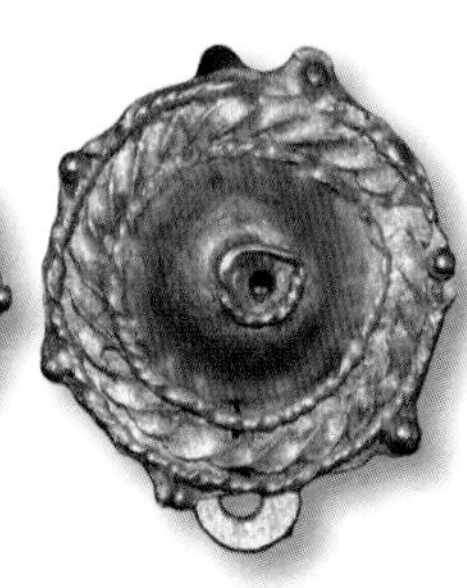

OJ-1868
Gold Earrings
26mm
Tutullus type
£200-£300

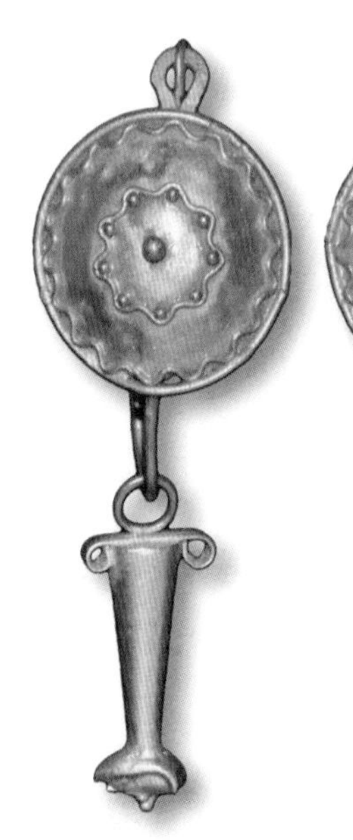

OJ-70751
Gold Earring Pair
48mm
£400-£600

OJ-54094
Earring Pair with Bead Dangles
38mm
£200-£300

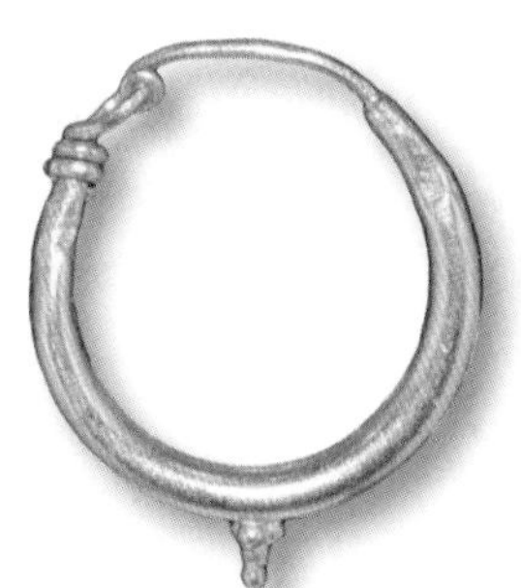

OJ-69753
Gold Hoop Earrings
19mm
£200-£300

OJ-7655
Gold Serpent Bracelet
95mm
From £800

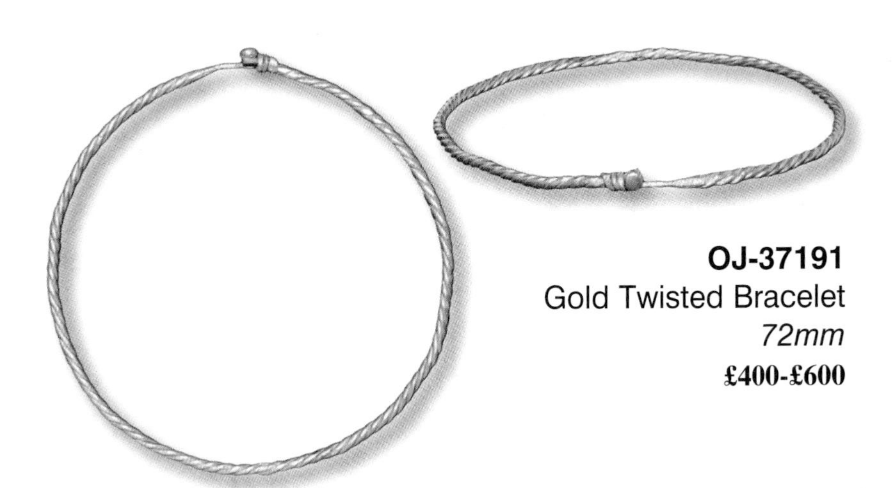

OJ-37191
Gold Twisted Bracelet
72mm
£400-£600

OJ-6559
Panther Bracelet
59mm
£150-£200

OJ-50482
Silver Serpent Bracelet
63mm
£80-£100

OJ-45988
Silver
Armilla
Bracelet
81mm
£150-£200

OJ-58945
Silver
Armilla
Bracelet
82mm
£80-£100

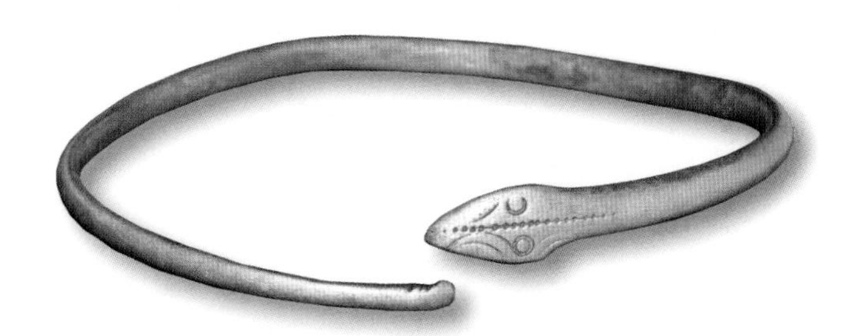

OJ-70263
Armilla
Military
Bracelet
58mm
£80-£100

OJ-57659
Armilla
Bracelet
53mm
£60-£80

OJ-57670
Armilla
Bracelet
53mm
£60-£80

OJ-6249
Armilla
Bracelet
76mm
£60-£80

OJ-53239
Armilla
Bracelet
75mm
£30-£40

OJ-42022
Armilla Bracelet
66mm
£50-£70

OJ-20987
Bracelet
67mm
£40-£60

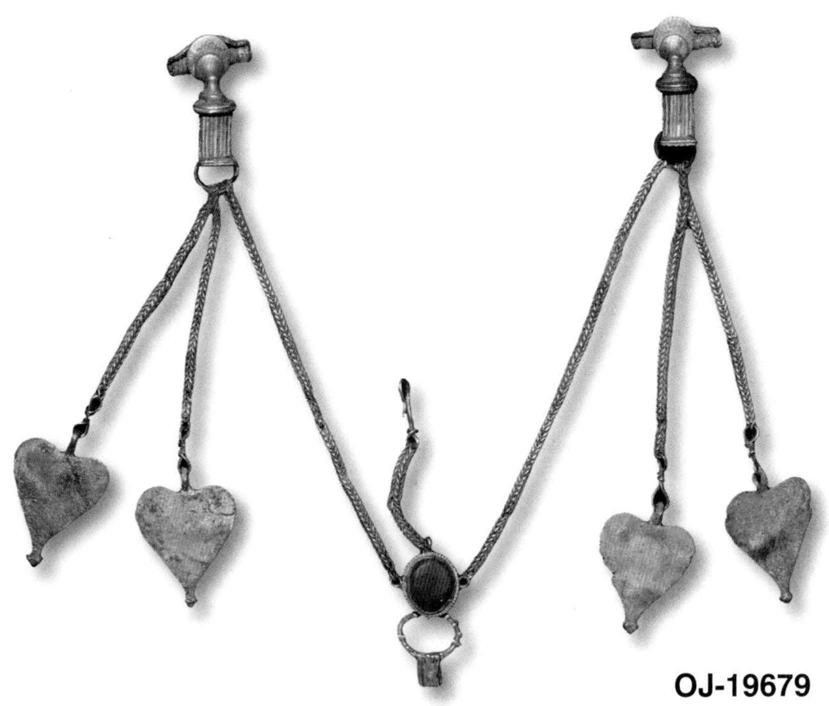

OJ-19679
Silver Military Insignia Pair
300mm
From £2,000

OJ-10069
Gold Hair Pin
70mm
£300-£400

OJ-2470
Gold Fish-Headed Hair Pin
82mm
£200-£300

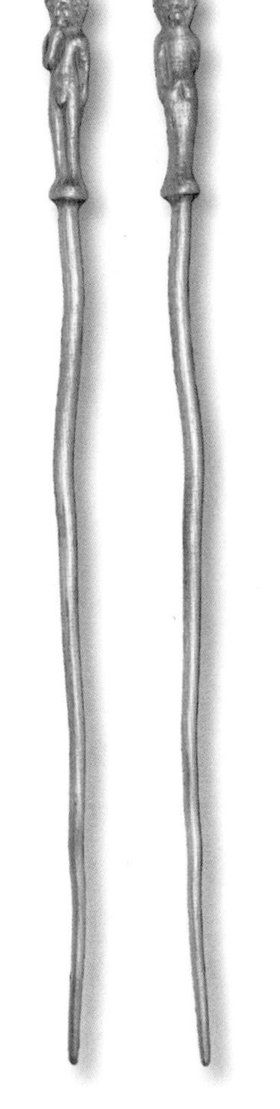

OJ-45085
Gold
Hairpin with
Harpocrates
130mm
£200-£300

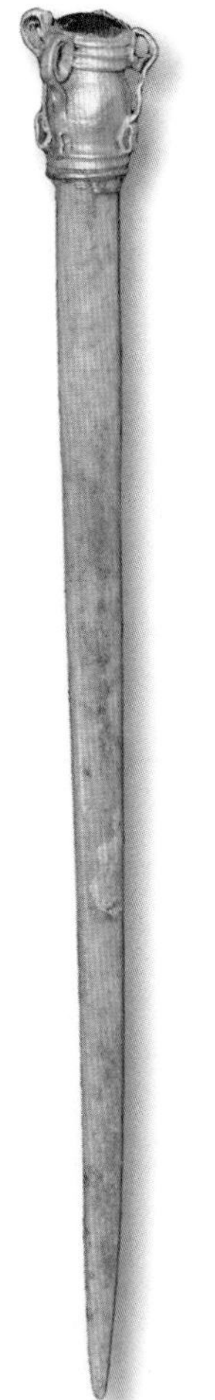

OJ-8196
Bone Dress Pin with Gold Fitting
117mm
£100-£150

OJ-1149
Silver-Gilt Silver Pin
140mm
With eagle finial
£300-£400

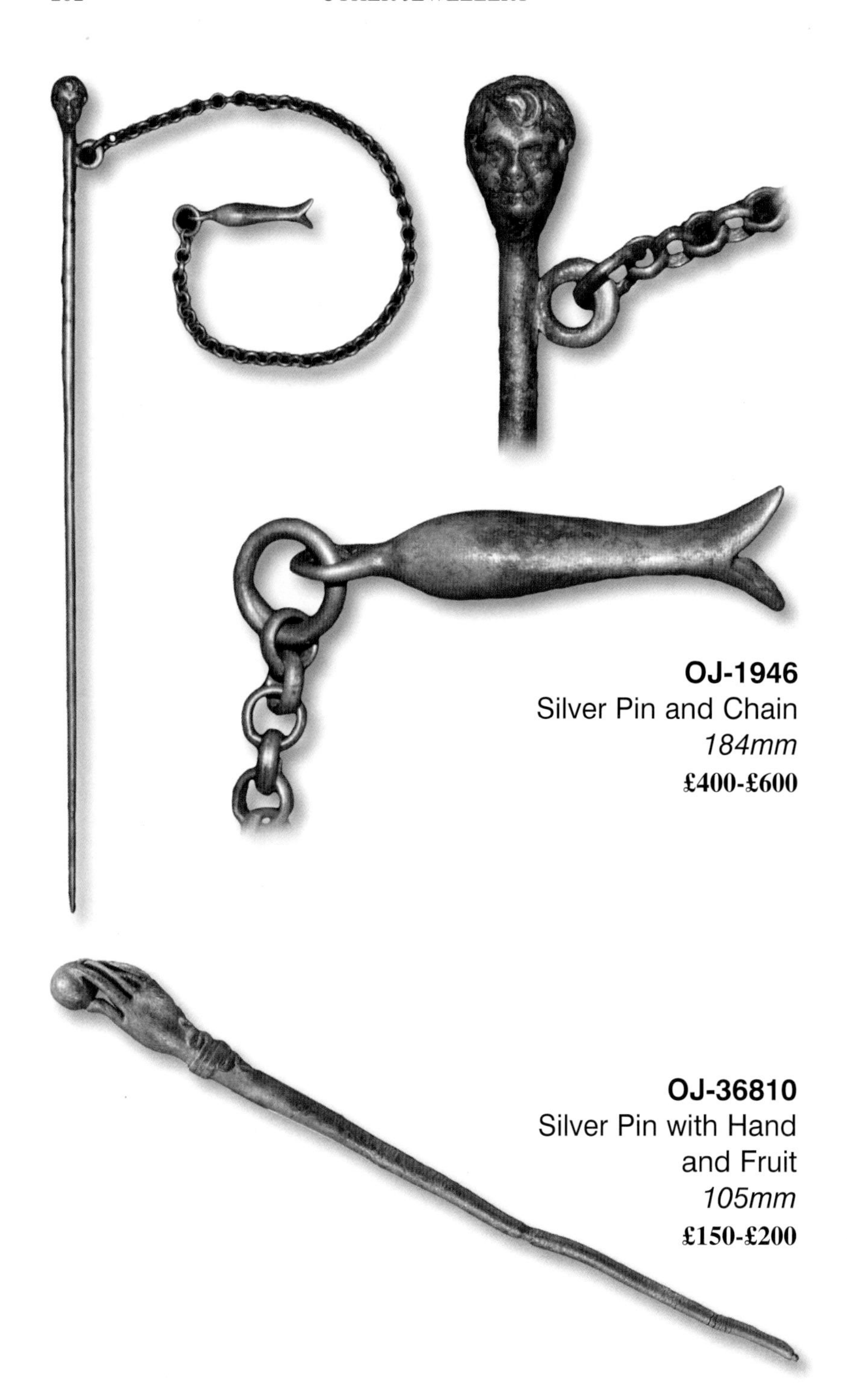

OJ-1946
Silver Pin and Chain
184mm
£400-£600

OJ-36810
Silver Pin with Hand and Fruit
105mm
£150-£200

OJ-16450
Silver Dress Pin
115mm
Bust finial possibly
Emperor Claudius
(ruled 41-54 AD)
£200-£300

OJ-31322
Silver Pin with Hand and Pearl
105mm
£150-£200

OJ-60467
Pin with Empress's Head
105mm
Possibly Julia Domna (170-217 AD)
£100-£150

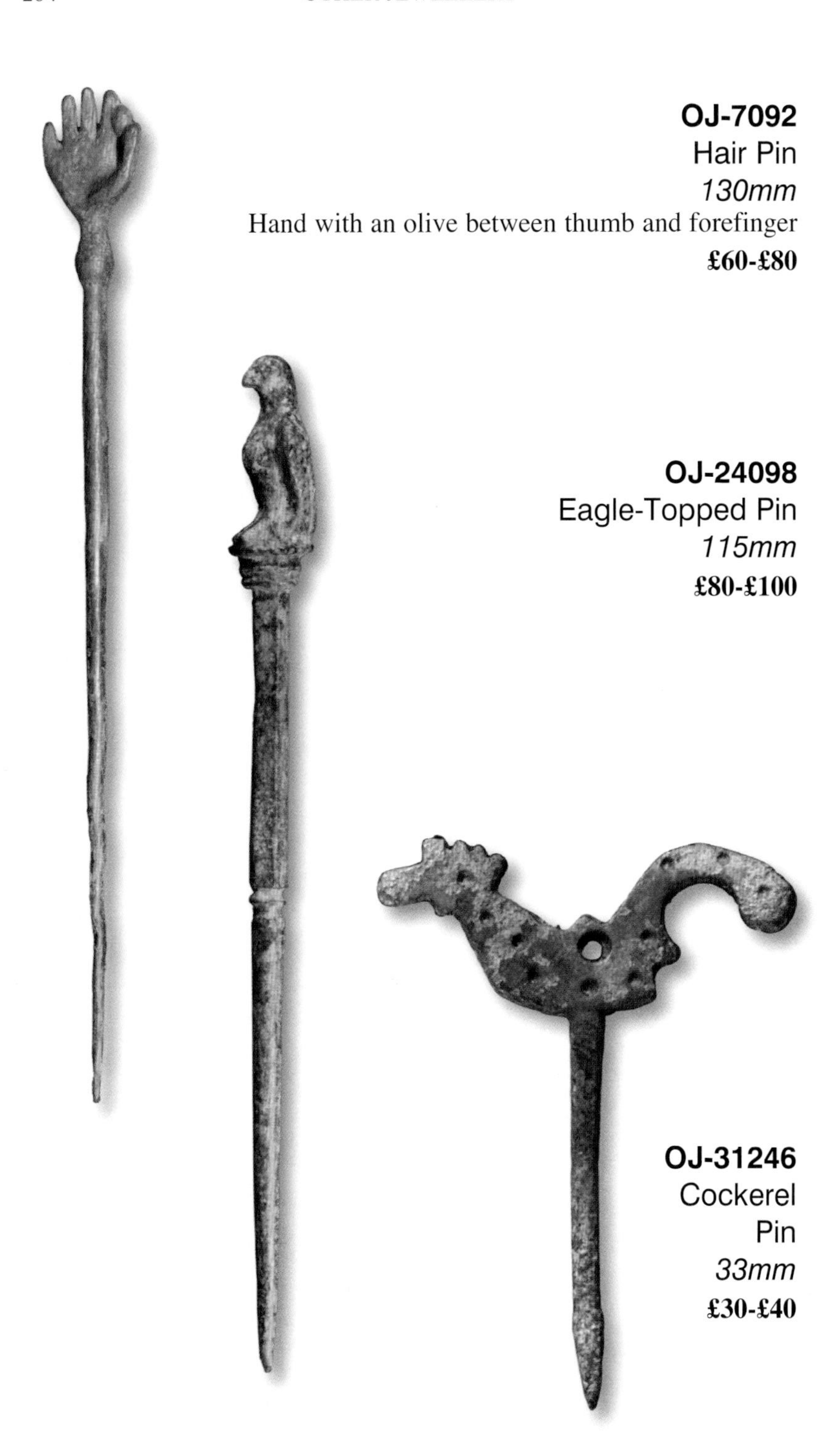

OJ-7092
Hair Pin
130mm
Hand with an olive between thumb and forefinger
£60-£80

OJ-24098
Eagle-Topped Pin
115mm
£80-£100

OJ-31246
Cockerel
Pin
33mm
£30-£40

OJ-52326
Minerva Cameo
17mm
£200-£300

OJ-57138
Intaglio with Portrait of Germanicus
12mm
£200-£300

BELTS & ACCESSORIES

In Roman culture, the wearing of a belt was initially restricted to the military although some civilian officials took up the practice towards the end of the Roman period. Belts were provided with a range of metal studs and mounts which served to stiffen the leather and to provide surfaces for ornament and display. The 'propeller' type is a very common find on military sites.

Belt buckles developed over time from relatively simple forms with a circular or square frame and spiked tongue into the elaborate Late Roman examples with a large rectangular surrounding frame and chip-carved ornament with a counter-plate to sit alongside the main plaque.

Sturdy leather belts provided protection for the midriff and groin with dangling straps (pteruges) and other elements. The full weight of mail or scale armour could be relieved from the shoulders if the belt were clasped tightly around the waist.

BA-21651
Buckle and Hinged Plate
101mm
Ornate scrolled detailing
£80-£050

BA-6562
Buckle
100mm
Scrolled buckle loop
£80-£100

BA-27424
Buckle Plate
80mm
Running tendrils design
£80-£100

BA-52800
Gilt Buckle
50mm
Scrolls and disc on the plate
£100-£150

BA-51806
Buckle
82mm
Latticework plate
£100-£150

BA-65283
Buckle and Counterplate
51-70mm
Double-tongued type
£300-£400

BA-61926
Buckle
35mm
Raised lobes and tendrils
£30-£40

BA-21717
Buckle
41mm
Human mask motif
£60-£80

BA-59435
Buckle
86mm
Raised leaf motif
£30-£40

BA-37490
Buckle Plate
81mm
Late Roman military type
£150-£200

BA-37493
Buckle Plate
66mm
Late Roman military type
£300-£400

BA-28749
Belt Stiffener
54mm
Propeller within frame type
£30-£40

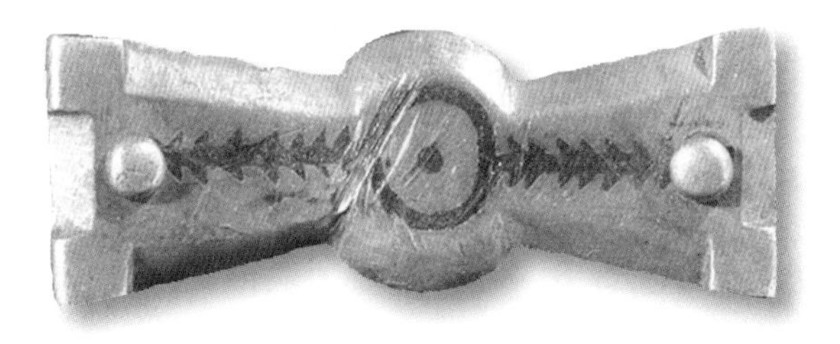

BA-56499
Silver Belt Stiffener
27mm
Propeller type
£80-£100

BA-17766
Strap End
38mm
Inscribed 'ABEFDRX/ XSNRFF/MII'
£120-£180

BA-65971

Silver Belt Suite

53-78mm

Openwork 'VTERE FELIX' (use [this] happily) legend

From £500

MOUNTS & APPLIQUÉS

Cast bronze mounts with a securing stud to the reverse were used to decorate and to protect, attached to both leather and wooden items.

Many mounts feature some such decorative motif as a human face, a putto, the head of Medusa or the bust of a young woman. Other common themes are concentric circles and the phallus. In some cases these motifs may have been amuletic, while others were probably purely ornamental. Geometric forms were also popular since they could be combined to cover any surface efficiently.

Bronze and gilded mounts are particularly associated with the Roman army in which it was important to make an impressive display in order to overawe enemies and potential allies.

MN-18311
Couple
Appliqué
160mm
Funerary images
of a couple
£800-£1,000

MN-14751
Scabbard
Mount
120mm
Galloping
horseman image
£200-£300

MN-22908
Figural Mount
74mm
Hermes / Mercury type
From £1,000

MN-7078
Bust
Mount
57mm
Mercury in
petasos
£300-£400

MN-21715
Mount
105mm
Isis Fortuna type
£400-£600

MN-35320
Bust Appliqué
54mm
Bust of Mercury
£120-£180

MN-6759
Bust Mount
53mm
Bust of Mercury
£80-£100

MN-20279
Bust Mount
52mm
Bust of Mars in helmet
£150-£200

MN-58948
Bust Mount
45mm
Bust of Mars in helmet
£150-£200

MN-26361
Mount of Minerva
75mm
Minerva in helmet
£300-£400

MN-8809
Mercury Bust Mount
40mm
Mercury in helmet
£100-£150

MN-20969
Minerva Bust Mount
37mm
£40-£60

MN-66173
Appliqué with Bust
29mm
Military figure in helmet
£120-£180

MN-22661
Campaign Tripod Table Mount
81mm
Gladiator or helmeted figure
£100-£150

MN-35775
Silver Pectoral Mount
105mm
Mask of Medusa
£150-£200

MN-2219
Gorgon Mount
71mm
Mask of Medusa
£120-£180

MN-45938
Mask Mount
47mm
Mask of Medusa
£80-£100

MN-23215
Mask Mount
44mm
Mask of Medusa
£80-£100

MN-26919
Mask Mount
54mm
Mask of Medusa
£80-£100

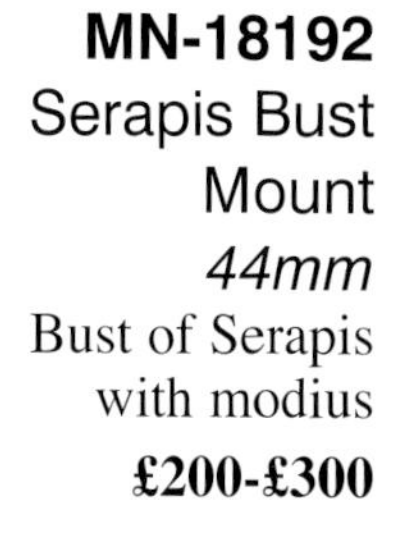

MN-18192
Serapis Bust Mount
44mm
Bust of Serapis with modius
£200-£300

MN-7455
Serapis Mount
90mm
Bust of Serapis with modius
£400-£600

MN-5707
Seated Priapus Mount
58mm
Priapus with food balanced on his phallus
£200-£300

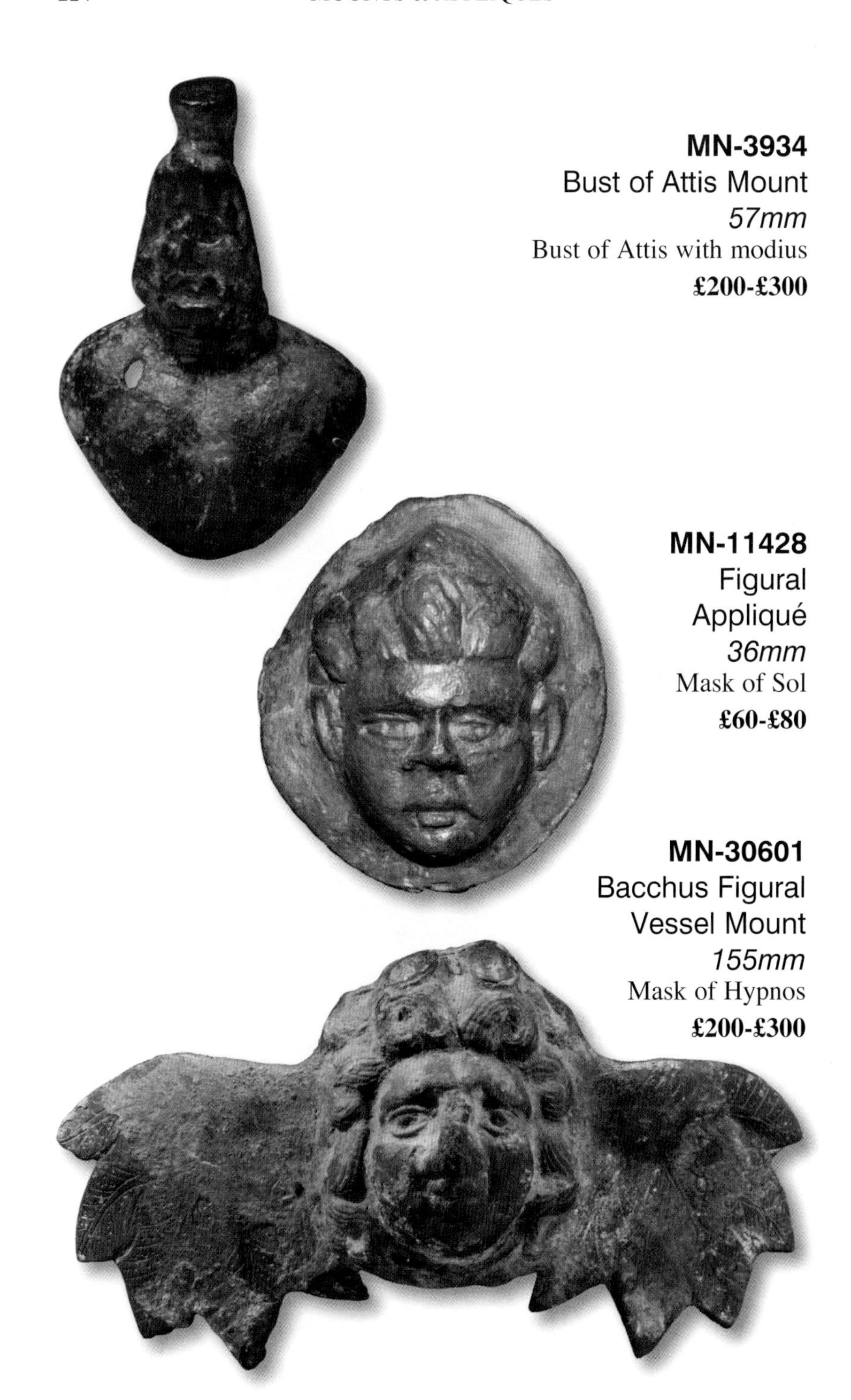

MN-3934
Bust of Attis Mount
57mm
Bust of Attis with modius
£200-£300

MN-11428
Figural
Appliqué
36mm
Mask of Sol
£60-£80

MN-30601
Bacchus Figural
Vessel Mount
155mm
Mask of Hypnos
£200-£300

MN-66174
Bust Appliqué
32mm
Vestal Virgin type
£150-£200

MN-65261
Bacchante Appliqué
64mm
With silver-inlaid eyes
£150-£200

MN-10392
Bacchus
Appliqué
45mm
Mask with ivy
£150-£200

MN-14773
Head Appliqué
41mm
Bust of Dionysus
£200-£300

MN-40896
Bacchus Appliqué
60mm
With glass inlaid eyes
£120-£180

MN-57631
Bacchus Mount
45mm
Bacchus with
vineleaves in his hair
£150-£200

MN-65754
Bacchus Vessel Mount
65mm
Bacchus with vineleaves in his hair
£100-£150

MN-19373
Bacchus Bucket Mount
68mm
Bacchus with vineleaves in his hair
£80-£100

MN-28782
Bacchus Bust Mount
54mm
Bacchus with vineleaves in his hair
£60-£80

MN-19648
Dionysus Head Mount
20mm
Bearded with elaborate hairstyle
£80-£100

MN-19641
Head of Apollo Appliqué
34mm
Apollo with youthful features
£100-£150

MN-20970
Apollo Bust Mount
37mm
Plaque and head modelled in the round
£40-£60

MN-25290
Jupiter Bust Mount
38mm
Helmeted and bearded head
£60-£80

MN-35496
Jupiter Ammon Bust Appliqué
46mm
Jupiter Ammon, bearded and with curled hair and ram's horns, in the original matrix
£100-£150

MN-35830
Mount with Silver Roundel
36mm
Silver appliqué with a high-relief scene of Silenus and a horse
£150-£200

MN-13769
Silenus Mount
31mm
Silenus with silver eye
£120-£180

MN-48892
Silenus Mount
57mm
Silenus with fleshy features
£100-£150

MN-40035
Silenus Head Mount
14mm
Silenus with fleshy features
£30-£40

MN-27515
Satyr Mount
32mm
Bearded with fleshy features
£100-£150

MN-38987
Satyr Bowl
Mount
42mm
Hollow to
the reverse
£100-£150

MN-51497
Roundel with
Appliqué
53mm
Satyr mask type
£100-£150

MN-17989
Head of Pan Mount
83mm
Pan with tousled hair
£800-£1,000

MN-2232
Faunus Mount
31mm
Bust of Faunus with annulets on the neck suggesting a chain
£150-£200

MN-14761
Bust of Faunus Appliqué
45mm
Faunus bust with curly hair, curly beard and goat's ears
£150-£200

MN-57628
Pan Mount
37mm
Pan with thick hair and beard
£100-£150

MN-16216
Faunus Mount
35mm
Faunus with
youthful features
£80-£100

MN-52958
Eros Vessel Mount
60mm
Head of Eros on a
heart-shaped plaque
£80-£100

MN-17736
Putto Head Appliqué
31mm
Mask with fleshy features
£80-£100

MN-2035
Cupid Mount
52mm
Youthful features and dressed hair
£80-£100

MN-9336
Putto
Mount
49mm
Bronze putto figure with a bird
£80-£100

MN-62889
Lunate Bust Mount
41mm
Bronze male bust with crescent moon
£100-£150

MN-54682
Putto
Mount
46mm
Bronze mask
of a putto
£80-£100

MN-59273
Venus Mask Appliqué
28mm
Mask of Venus with dressed hair
£50-£70

MN-66030
Venus Face Mount
33mm
Mask of Venus with short hair
£40-£60

MN-20959
Belt Mount
40mm
High-relief head of Venus
£50-£70

MN-20516
Matrona Figural Mount
39mm
Mother and cat
£80-£100

MN-33993
Juno Appliqué
31mm
Bust of the youthful Juno
£40-£60

MN-18323
Face Appliqué
28mm
Youthful female mask
£40-£60

MN-4193
Face Mount
32mm
Youthful female mask
£40-£60

MN-6720
Empress Marciana Mount
56mm
Elder sister of Roman Emperor Trajan
£200-£300

MN-35316
Bowl Mount with Head of a Maenad
80mm
Facing female mask
£200-£300

MN-14982
Female Bust Appliqué
64mm
Facing female bust with elaborate hair
£150-£200

MN-20521
Female Bust Mount
36mm
Facing bust with mantle
£120-£180

MN-21718
Female
Athlete
Mount
77mm
Facing
female bust
£100-£150

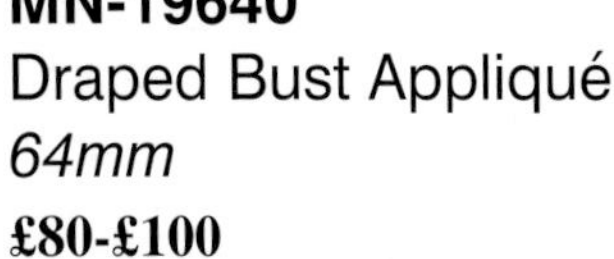

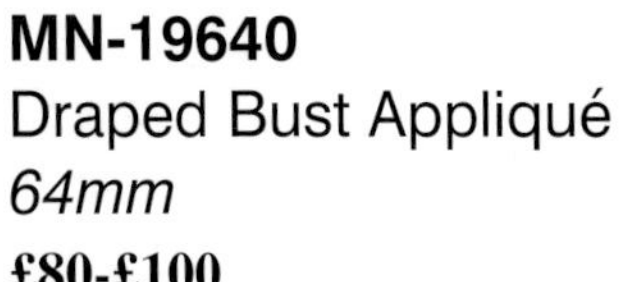

MN-19640
Draped Bust Appliqué
64mm
£80-£100

MN-58944
Actor's Mask Appliqué
36mm
'Comedy' with grinning mouth
£80-£100

MN-6317
Female Bust Mount
29mm
£60-£80

MN-1933
Female Bust Mount
45mm
£30-£40

MN-10290
Female Bust Bowl Mount
44mm
£30-£40

MN-30424
Erotic Mount
50mm
£80-£100

MN-18555
Female Bust Mount
54mm
£60-£80

MN-52830
Head Mount
46mm
Loop below
£80-£100

MN-10940
Miniature Bust Mount
31mm
Hercules bust
£50-£70

MN-26456
Mithras Head Mount
29mm
Mithras with conical cap
£60-£80

MN-67114

Military Figural Mount

54mm

Figure of Victory with spear

£80-£100

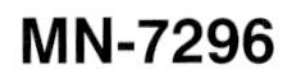

MN-7296

Head Mount

19mm

Facing mask

£40-£60

MN-40046

Goddess Mount

33mm

Facing female mask

£30-£40

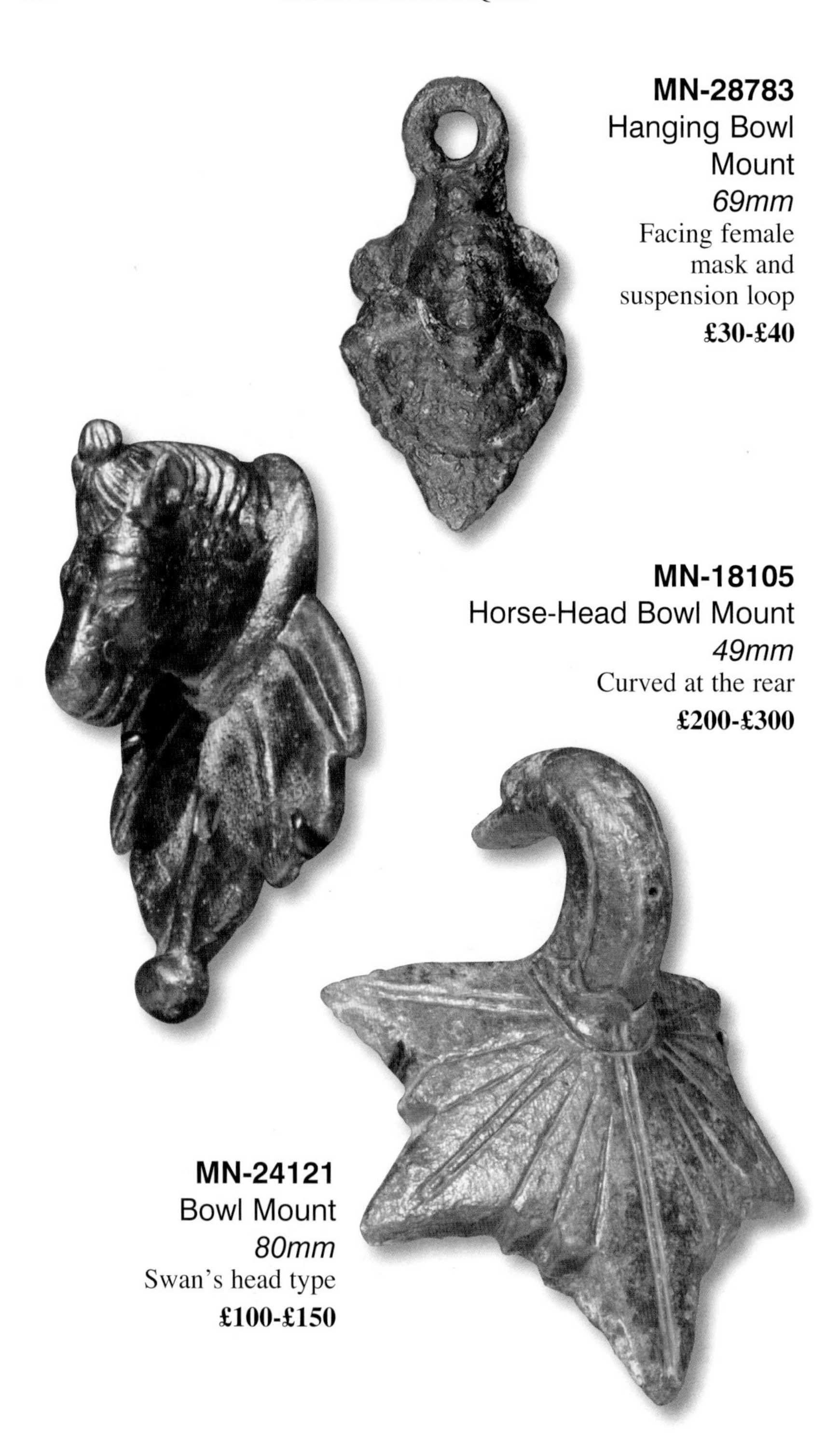

MN-28783
Hanging Bowl Mount
69mm
Facing female mask and suspension loop
£30-£40

MN-18105
Horse-Head Bowl Mount
49mm
Curved at the rear
£200-£300

MN-24121
Bowl Mount
80mm
Swan's head type
£100-£150

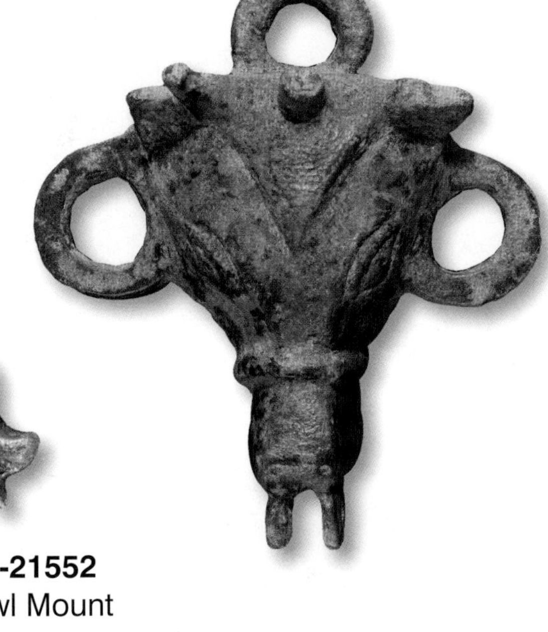

MN-18257

Bull's Head Mount

110mm

With loops to the ears and horns

£100-£150

MN-21552

Bowl Mount

55mm

Face-and-duck hook

£80-£100

MN-20522

Lion and Head Mount

50mm

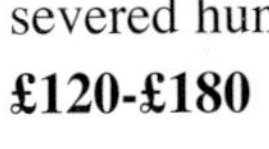

Lioness guarding a severed human head

£120-£180

MN-2439
Lion Mount
65mm
Crouching lion with forepaws extended
£80-£100

MN-3509
Mount
58mm
Pouncing lion type
£80-£100

MN-40724
Mask Casket Mount
35mm
Mask of a lion
£100-£150

MN-4789
Lion Head Mount
50mm
Lion mask
£100-£150

MN-31360
Lion Appliqué
60mm
Lion mask
£100-£150

MN-48196
Lion Head Appliqué
30mm
Lion mask
£80-£100

MN-45058
Lion Head Mount
39mm
Lion mask
£80-£100

MN-38772
Lion Head Mount
66mm
£100-£150

MN-3356
Lion Mask
32mm
£60-£80

MN-52954
Lion Mount
59mm
Lion's head and arched neck
£40-£60

MN-10286
Lion Head Mount
33mm
Open mouth
£30-£40

MN-17769
Silver Panther Head Mount
16mm
Feline mask
£150-£200

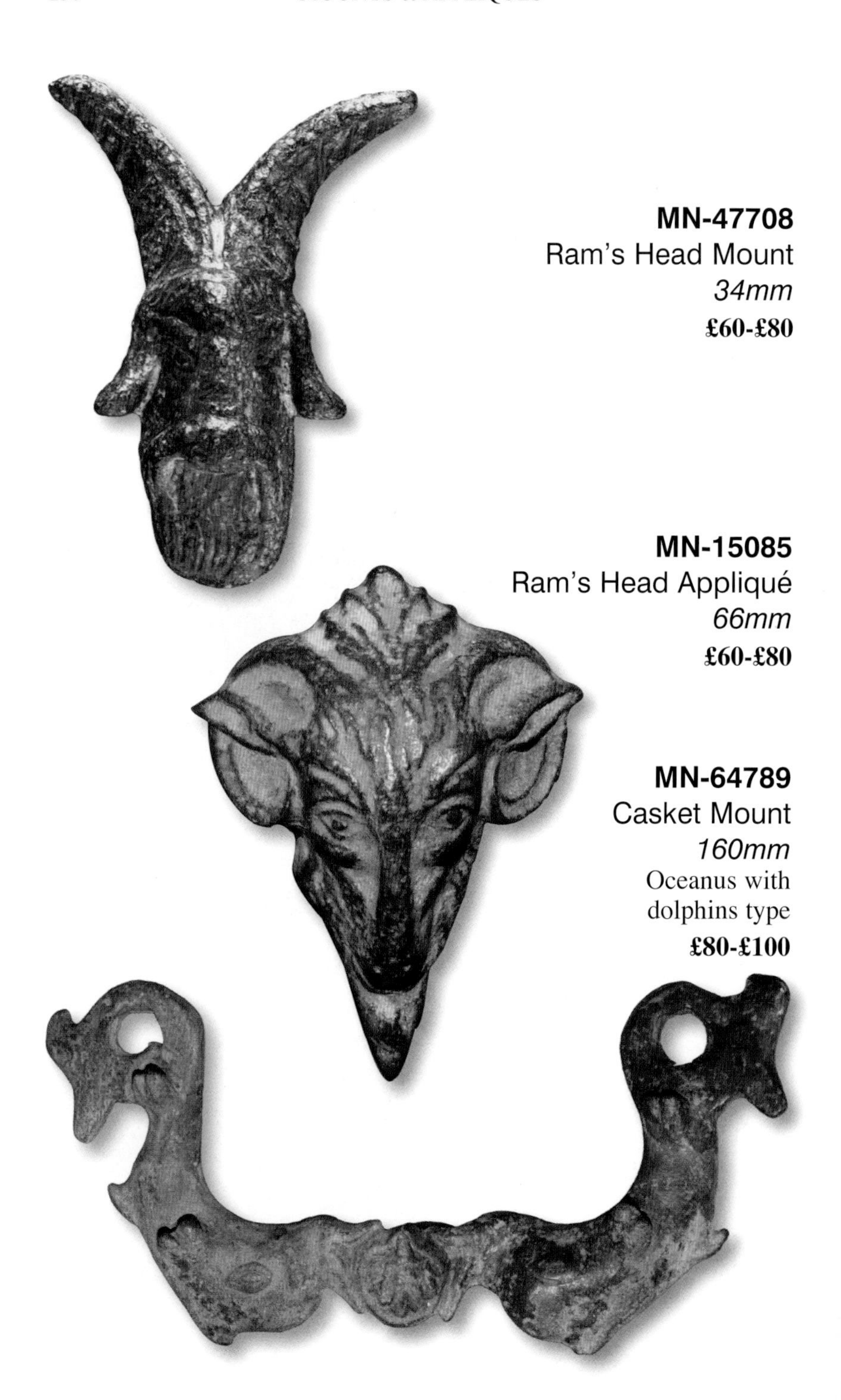

MN-47708
Ram's Head Mount
34mm
£60-£80

MN-15085
Ram's Head Appliqué
66mm
£60-£80

MN-64789
Casket Mount
160mm
Oceanus with dolphins type
£80-£100

MN-6566
Chariot Mount
100mm
Opposed dolphins
£80-£100

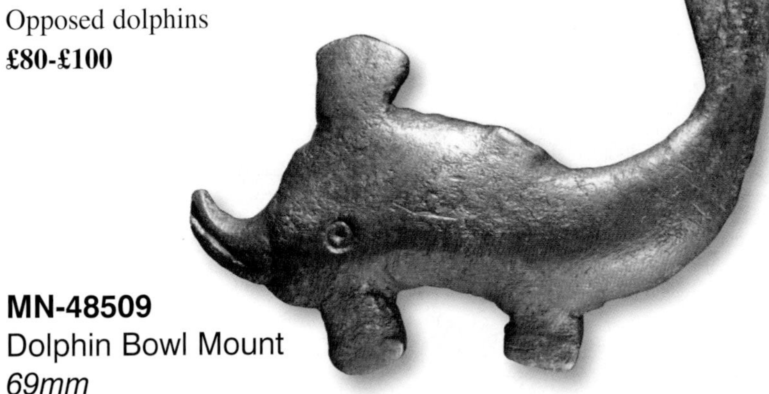

MN-48509
Dolphin Bowl Mount
69mm
£80-£100

MN-23249
Chariot
Mount
55mm
Dolphin mount
£60-£80

MN-16767
Eagle Mount
40mm
With wings spread
£80-£100

MN-28754
Cockerel Bowl Mount
38mm
Modelled in the round
£40-£60

MN-15675
Duck Mount
41mm
Modelled in the round
£30-£40

MN-4252
Chariot Mount
105mm
Two dolphins type
£80-£100

MN-37491
Belt Mount
66mm
Opposed lions type
£200-£300

MN-18376
Belt Mount
48mm
Millefiori panel
£200-£300

MN-60760
Phallic Mount
71mm
Male genitals modelled in the round
£200-£300

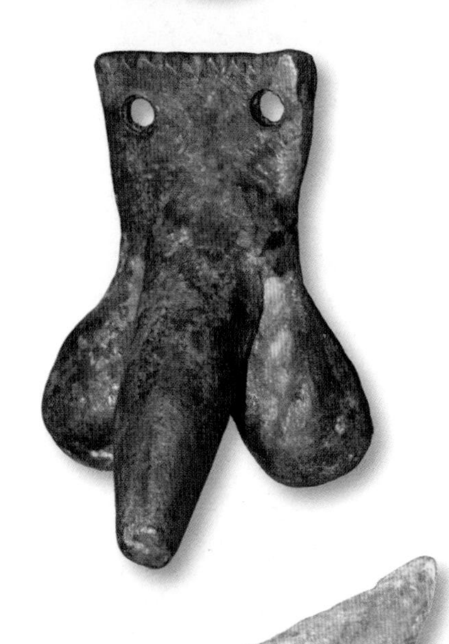

MN-63968
Phallic Mount
36mm
Male genitals modelled in the round
£100-£150

MN-24146
Phallic Mount
62mm
Male genitals modelled in the round
£60-£80

MN-18204
Phallic Mount
41mm
£40-£60

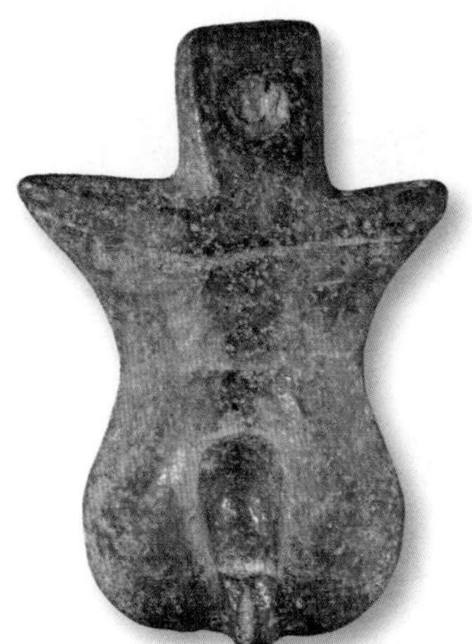

MN-61905
Phallic Whorl Mount
56mm
Four phalloi forming a sunwheel
£60-£80

MN-7677
Phallic Mount
49mm
£40-£60

MN-56227
Enamelled Mount
34mm
£60-£80

MN-7393
Shield Appliqué
39mm
£120-£180

MN-6744
Enamelled
Mount
66mm
£40-£60

PL-2747
Four Emperors Plaque
47mm
The Tetrarchs with wreaths and surrounding text
£800-£1,000

PL-19636
Thunderbolt Insignium Plaque
115mm
£300-£400

PL-4394
Putto and Bird Panel
110mm
£200-£300

PL-10966
Hercules Plaque
115mm
£100-£150

PL-16221
Boar’s Head
Plaque
72mm
£200-£300

PL-38752
Repoussé Plaque
35mm
Horse and rider type
£40-£60

PL-51117
Satyr Head Plaque
110mm
£300-£400

PL-66175
Inscribed Votive
Plaque
330mm
£80-£100

PL-69489
Niello-Inlaid Plaque
57mm
Rosette within a looped border
£60-£80

PL-4340
Figural Plaque
62mm
Head of Roma
£50-£70

PL-30805
Millefiori Disc
49mm
£50-£70

PL-24151
Flora Plaque
55mm
Silver-inlaid
£200-£300

PL-3304
Plaque
64mm
Bacchus bust
£100-£150

PL-10948
Plaque
43mm
Huntsman type
£100-£150

PL-52208
Plaque
36mm
Isis and Harpocrates
£150-£200

PL-4292
Figural
Plaque
94mm
Dionysus type
£400-£600

PL-4291
Plaque
76mm
Icon of Fortuna
£300-£400

ST-58949
Stud
39mm
Head of Medusa
£80-£100

ST-60860
Silver Stud with
Female Bust
13mm
£60-£800

ST-19632
Chi-Rho Stud
20mm
Incised Christogram
£70-£90

ST-38093
Enamelled Stud
25mm
Radiating panels
£50-£70

DOMESTIC ITEMS

Tableware and domestic items are a plentiful source of information about daily life in the Roman period. Every villa site yields quantities of dishes, jars, bowls and cups in a variety of ceramic fabrics, both local and imported. Stone bowls indicate access to craftsmen with appropriate cutting and grinding tools.

Likewise bronze platters and dishes show that access to casting was no longer confined to the very wealthiest members of society but rather became available to relatively modest households.

Cutlery, including spoons and table knives, may often be well designed, made in silver or bronze and with detailed ornament. Swan-neck spoons are a long-lived fashion which could be purely functional or highly decorated and ostentatious, some with a short text on the handle.

Lamps made in terracotta or bronze are an evolving form of utensil which can reveal evidence for the date of manufacture and the owner's status. Sometimes figures of beasts or humans are included in the decorative scheme as well as rosettes, tendrils, scrolls and other ornament.

Bowls and dishes made in silver with repoussé decoration reveal something of the pre-occupations of their users, including heroic legends and hunting scenes. The handles of these vessels often survive independent of the bowls and display animal and other forms. Bowls were sometimes suspended on ropes or chains using applied mounts, often with a human or animal head.

Glassware of various kinds completed the dining experience for the wealthy Roman or the local magnate affecting Roman manners. Flasks, sprinklers, cups and various bottles form part of the range of glass containers available to a well-run household.

Ceramic and glass vessels are a popular choice for collectors, especially where the decoration indicates religious or social roles.

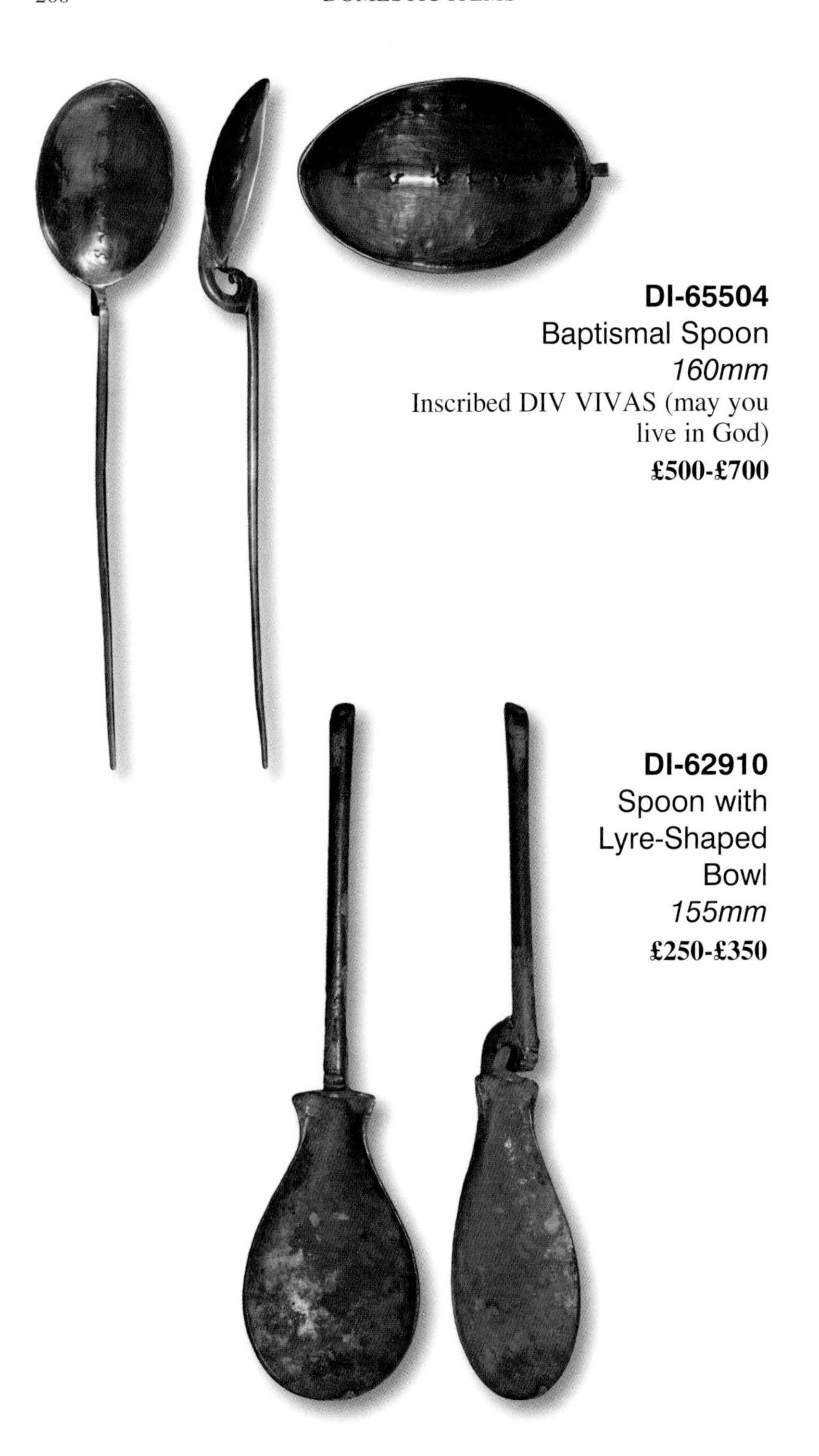

DI-65504
Baptismal Spoon
160mm
Inscribed DIV VIVAS (may you live in God)
£500-£700

DI-62910
Spoon with Lyre-Shaped Bowl
155mm
£250-£350

DI-65312
Swan-Necked Spoon
160mm
Bull-head detail on the handle
From £300

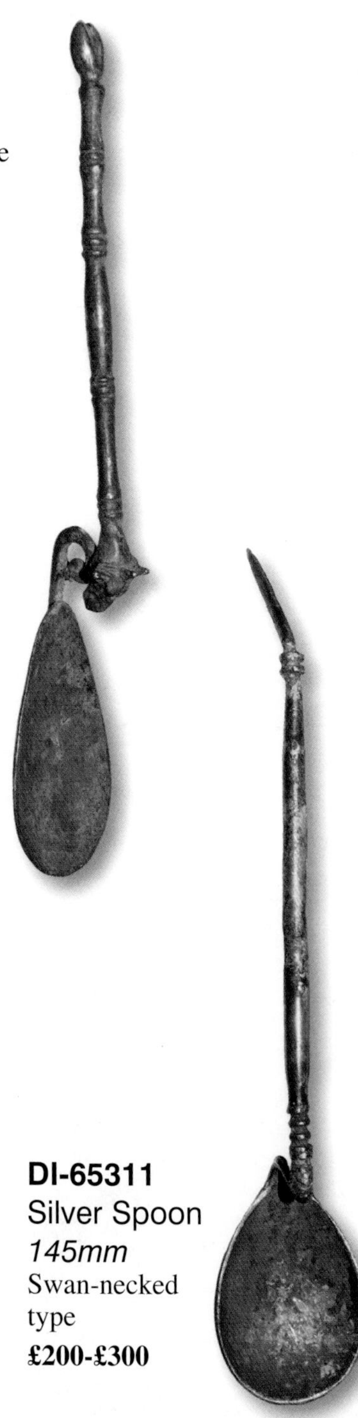

DI-50370
Silver
Spoon
145mm
Incised cross
From £400

DI-65311
Silver Spoon
145mm
Swan-necked
type
£200-£300

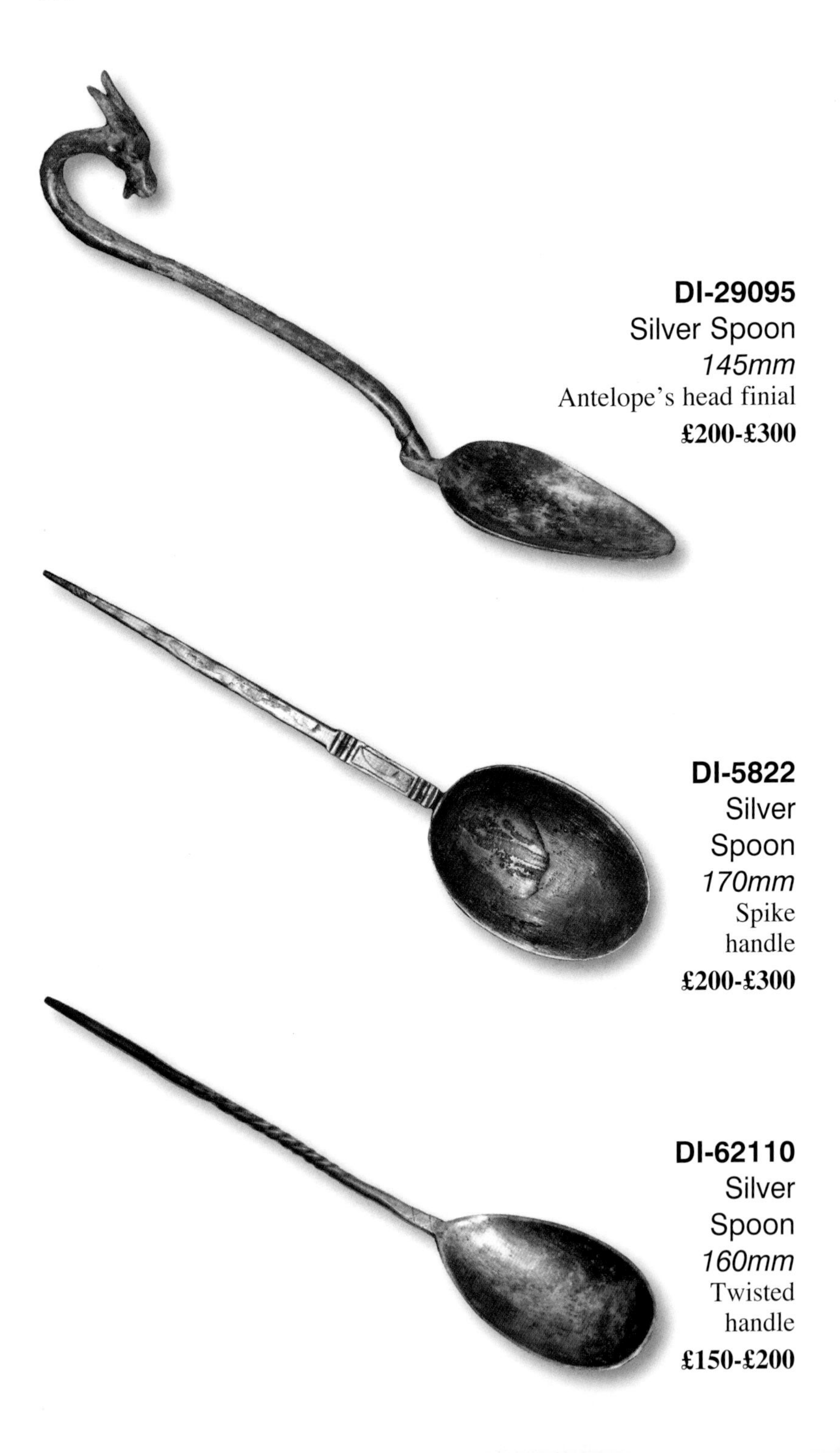

DI-29095
Silver Spoon
145mm
Antelope's head finial
£200-£300

DI-5822
Silver
Spoon
170mm
Spike
handle
£200-£300

DI-62110
Silver
Spoon
160mm
Twisted
handle
£150-£200

DI-50371
Spoon with Swan-Neck Handle
155mm
Spike handle
£150-£200

DI-2495
Silver Spoon
151mm
Dolphin type
£120-£180

DI-51810
Swan-Necked Spoon
140mm
Horse's hoof finial
£200-£300

DI-51809
Spoon
135mm
Stylus or spike handle
£120-£180

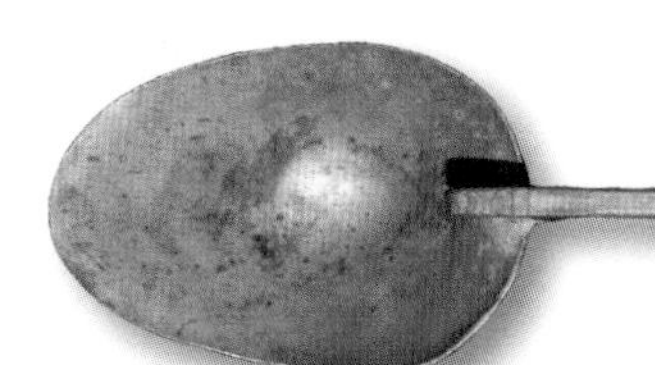

DI-7154
Silver Swan-Neck Spoon
200mm
Scrolled openwork junction with rib beneath
£120-£180

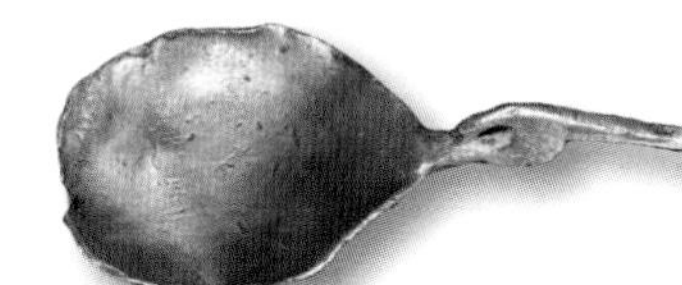

DI-4783
Silver Spoon
120mm
Swan-neck with bird-head decoration
£100-£150

DI-11906
Silver Spoon
165mm
Junction with stem and knop decoration
£100-150

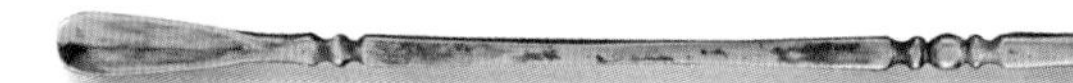

DI-29796
Silver-Gilt Unguent Spoon
190mm
Medical or cosmetic type
£200-£300

DI-42039
Silver Spoon
43mm
Recurved handle
£100-£150

DI-57123
Strainer Spoon
110mm
Perforated bowl
£250-£350

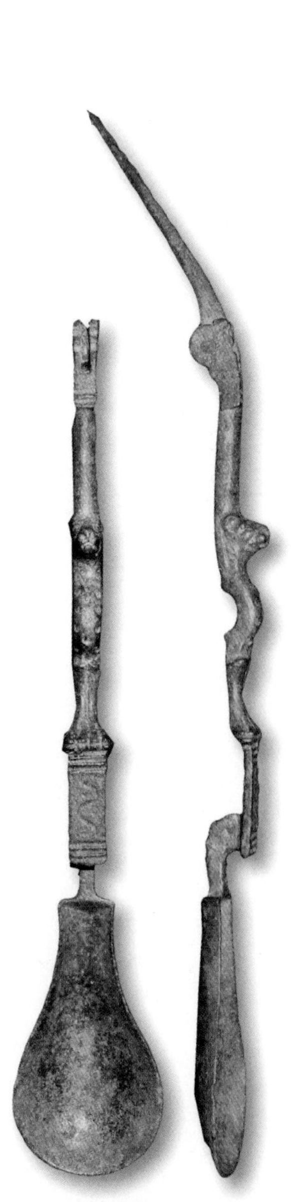

DI-38742
Strainer
Spoon
115mm
Perforated
bowl
£80-£100

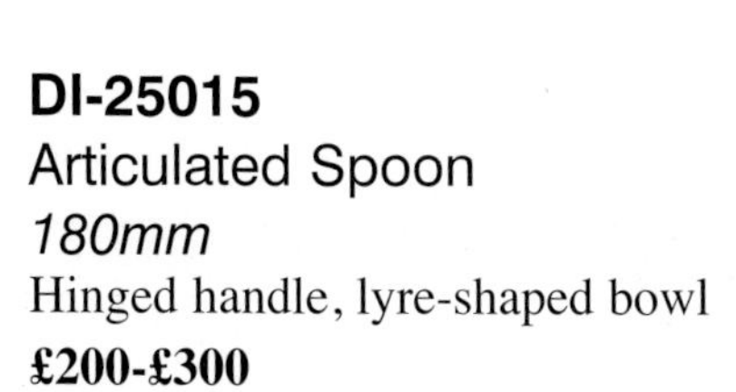

DI-25015
Articulated Spoon
180mm
Hinged handle, lyre-shaped bowl
£200-£300

DI-9782
Spoon
160mm
Dolphin type
£100-£150

DI-57700
Spoon
215mm
Lion type
£100-£150

DI-36369
Bronze Swan-Necked Spoon
160mm
Tinned surface
£120-£180

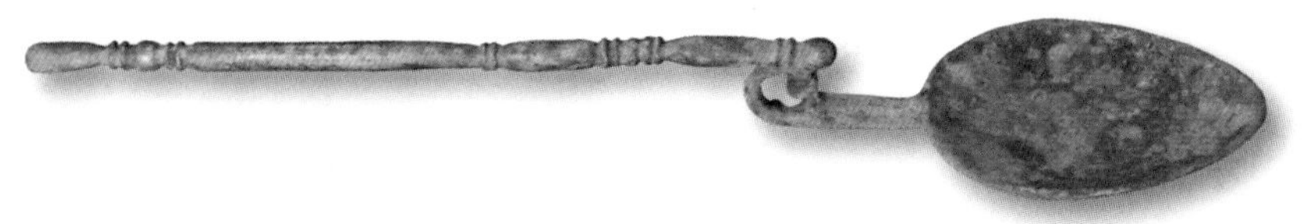

DI-26402
Swan-Necked Spoon
170mm
Lyre-shaped bowl
£100-£150

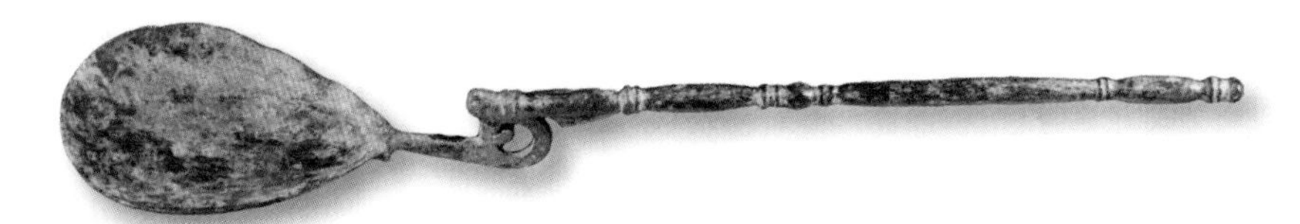

DI-26403

Spoon

165mm

Swan-necked type

£100-£150

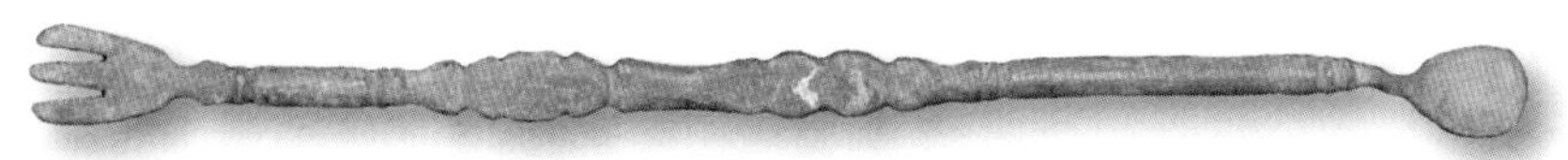

DI-4724

Spoon and Fork Utensil

130mm

Bowl to one end and trident to the other

£80-£100

DI-65244

Hooked
Fork

540mm

Twisted Shaft

£150-£200

DI-64701

Inlaid Fork

150mm

Nacre panels

£40-£60

DI-32149
Ladle
185mm
Balustered handle
£100-£150

DI-31543
Silver Bowl
175mm
Hunting Scenes in repoussé work
From £5,000

DI-3732
Silvered Drinking Cup
100mm
Repoussé acorn and oakleaf designs
From £400

DI-67067
Bronze Cup
55mm
Bell-shaped profile
£100-£140

DI-45915
Miniature Bowl
57mm
£100-£150

DI-26918
Miniature Bowl
57mm
£100-£150

DI-24216
Bowl
210mm
£100-£150

DI-68343
Serving Plate
430mm
Tinned surface,
ledge handles
£500-£700

DI-46461
Tinned
Bronze Dish
115mm
Flange rim
£150-£200

DI-13967
Bronze Platter
345mm
Concentric rings
£150-£200

DI-1209
Decorated Red Ware Platter
316mm
Concentric rings and central rosette
£150-£200

DI-17899
Marble Platter
395mm
Chamfered rim
From £500

DI-32874
Stone Mortar
175mm
£100-£150

DI-47748
Wine Strainer
250mm
Perforated bowl
£300-£400

DI-54670
Domed Strainer
115mm
£100-£150

DI-57790
Pouring Vessel
220mm
Handle in the form of an arm with armlet and bracelet
£200-£300

DI-57775
Pouring Vessel
260mm
Ribbed bowl
£200-£300

DI-46084
Large Handled Ewer
205mm
Strap handle and rolled rim
£300-£400

DI-38965
Bronze Wine Jug
190mm
Raised thumb-pad
£200-£300

DI-28822
Ewer
240mm
Deep shoulder and flared lip
£150-£200

DI-3074
Bronze
Miniature Ewer
101mm
Broad pouring lip
£100-£150

DI-3394
Glass Sprinkler
Flask
68mm
Squat body and
loop handle
£80-£100

DI-2982
Glass
Sprinkler Flask
78mm
Dimpled body
£60-£80

DI-20496
Gladiator's
Oil Jar
380mm
Loops
flanking the
neck, drop
handle
From £1,500

DI-6393
Hanging Kettle
250mm
Elaborate drop handle
£400-£600

DI-3297
Wine Cup Stand
170mm
With lion's paw feet
£200-£300

DI-67142
Vessel Stand
26cm
Feet formed as lion's paws
£200-£300

DI-27426
Vessel Support
125mm
Dolphins and trident detailing
£300-£400

DI-20064
Large Cooking Pan
345mm
£120-£180

DI-3783
Upchurch Greyware Vessel
280mm
Broad flared rim
£100-£150

DI-57528
Ampulla
37mm
Stamped winged figure of Victory
£100-£150

DI-40218
Patera
345mm
Ram's head handle
From £1500

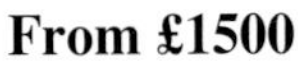

DI-45584
Patera
280mm
Concentric circle design
£250-£350

DI-29848
Patera
225mm
Twisted handle
£150-£200

DI-32185
Patera
280mm
Zoomorphic handle
£120-£180

DI-18316
Patera
83mm
Apollo, lyre and Victory
£100-£150

DI-30582
Bronze Patera
190mm
£80-£100

DI-48889
Patera Handle
145mm
Figural detail
£200-£300

DI-61890
Patera Handle
160mm
Ram's head type
£100-£150

DI-7419
Patera Handle
150mm
Ram's head type
£100-£150

DI-35851
Patera
Handle
140mm
Ram's head
type
£100-£150

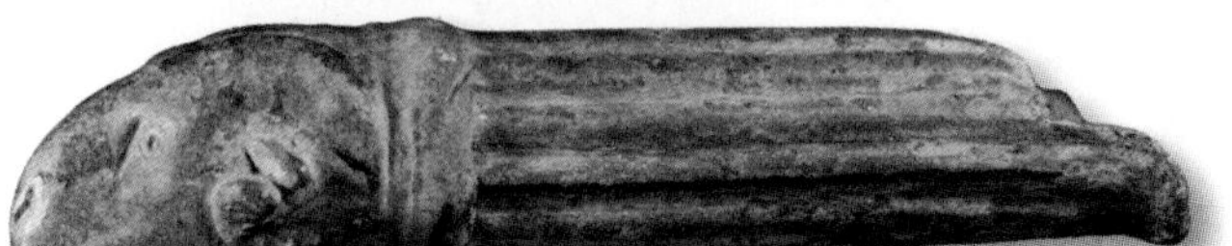

DI-19638
Ram Patera
Handle
120mm
Ram's head type
£80-£100

DI-5371
Phalera
82mm
Face of the river-god Achelous
From £2,500

DI-46508
Phalera
93mm
Medusa head
From £2,000

DI-3068
Phalera pair
115-117mm
Female busts
From £1,000

DI-61607
Phalera
63mm
Mask of Medusa
£600-£800

DI-9777
Phalera with Portrait
36mm
Female bust
£300-£400

DI-17988
Phalera
82mm
Mask of Medusa
£300-£400

DI-54679
Phalera
85mm
Horseman
(Alexander the
Great?)
85mm
£200-£300

DI-61421
Phalera
67mm
Lion in profile
£200-£300

DI-4811
Phalera
62mm
Mask of Medusa
£100-£150

DI-4048
Phalera
67mm
Mask of Medusa
£100-£150

DI-14895
Phalera
58mm
Mask of Medusa
£80-£100

DI-3289
Phalera
38mm
Head of Apollo
£60-£80

DI-65802
Phalera
48mm
Mask of Medusa
£40-£60

DI-27419
Phalera
72mm
Concentric rings design
£40-£60

DI-57383
Oil Lamp
155mm
Bull's head type
From £1,000

DI-41797
Oil Lamp with Bird Lid
325mm
Tripod stand
From £500

DI-42441
Oil Lamp
73mm
Swan type
From £400

DI-37174
Oil Lamp
125mm
Reflector plate on the handle
From £300

DI-69812
Porpoise Lamp
135mm
Bronze lamp with loop handle
£400-£600

DI-16218
Lunar Oil Lamp
120mm
Reflector plate on the handle
£300-£400

DI-51503
Oil Lamp
175mm
Loop handle
£200-£300

DI-61933
Double-Spouted Oil Lamp
190mm
Lateral nozzles, pierced suspension lugs
£150-£200

DI-514
Oil Lamp
110mm
Bronze with panther motif
£200-£300

DI-68303
Oil Lamp
90mm
Leaping lion motif
£100-£140

DI-58472
Oil Lamp Lid
45mm
Squatting female type
£150-£200

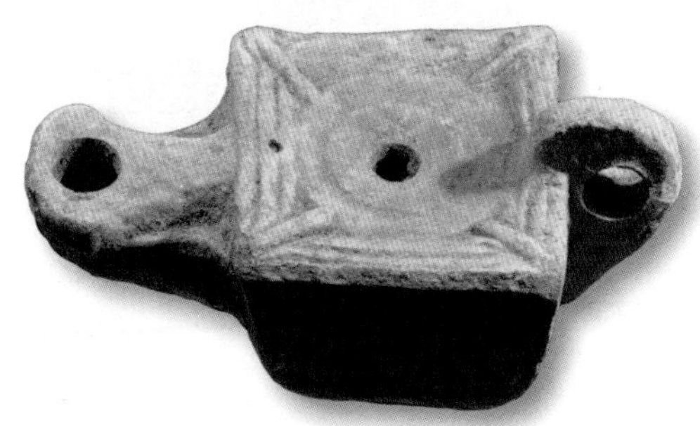

DI-60703
Square Oil Lamp
85mm
Loop handle
£60-£80

DI-11337
Oil Lamp Filler
120mm
Bowl with channel to the flange
£40-£60

DI-4836
Incense
Burner
110mm
Bowl with lion-head feet
£300-£400

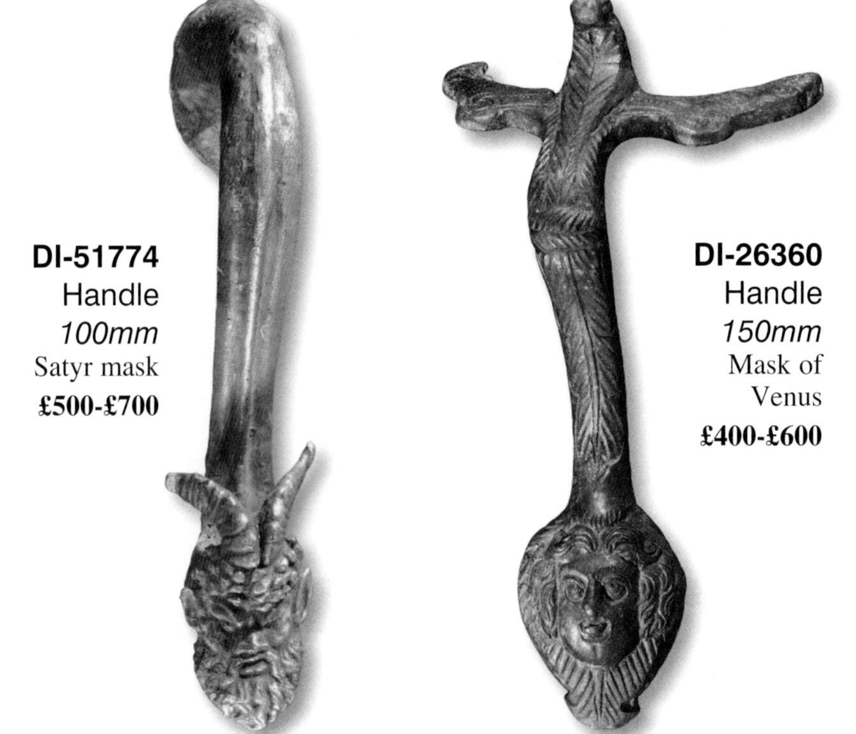

DI-51774
Handle
100mm
Satyr mask
£500-£700

DI-26360
Handle
150mm
Mask of Venus
£400-£600

DI-39063
Handle
150mm
Bacchus and horse-head terminal
£400-£600

DI-51125
Vessel
Handle
190mm
Face of
Odysseus/
Ulysses
£300-£400

DI-65757
Vessel Handle
84mm
Lion mask type
£300-£400

DI-29978
Vessel Handle
200mm
Right hand with spread fingers and thumb
£300-£400

DI-8679
Handle
105mm
Satyr figurine
£150-£200

DI-63602
Tankard Handle
68mm
Mask of Bacchus
£100-£150

DI-61891
Handle
140mm
Mask of Cupid
£100-£150

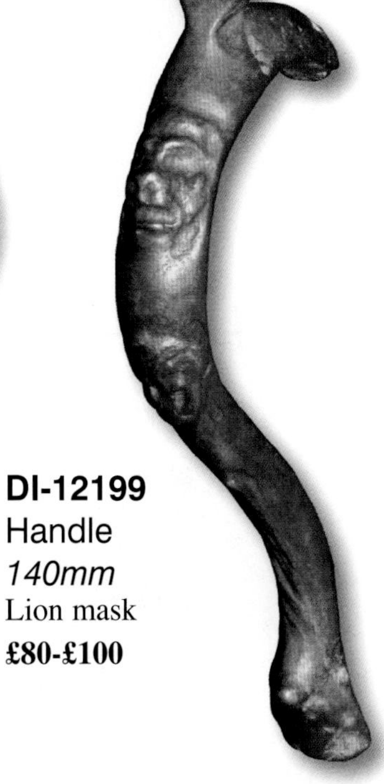

DI-12199
Handle
140mm
Lion mask
£80-£100

DI-18303
Hand Shovel Handle
200mm
Collar and D-shaped blade
£80-£100

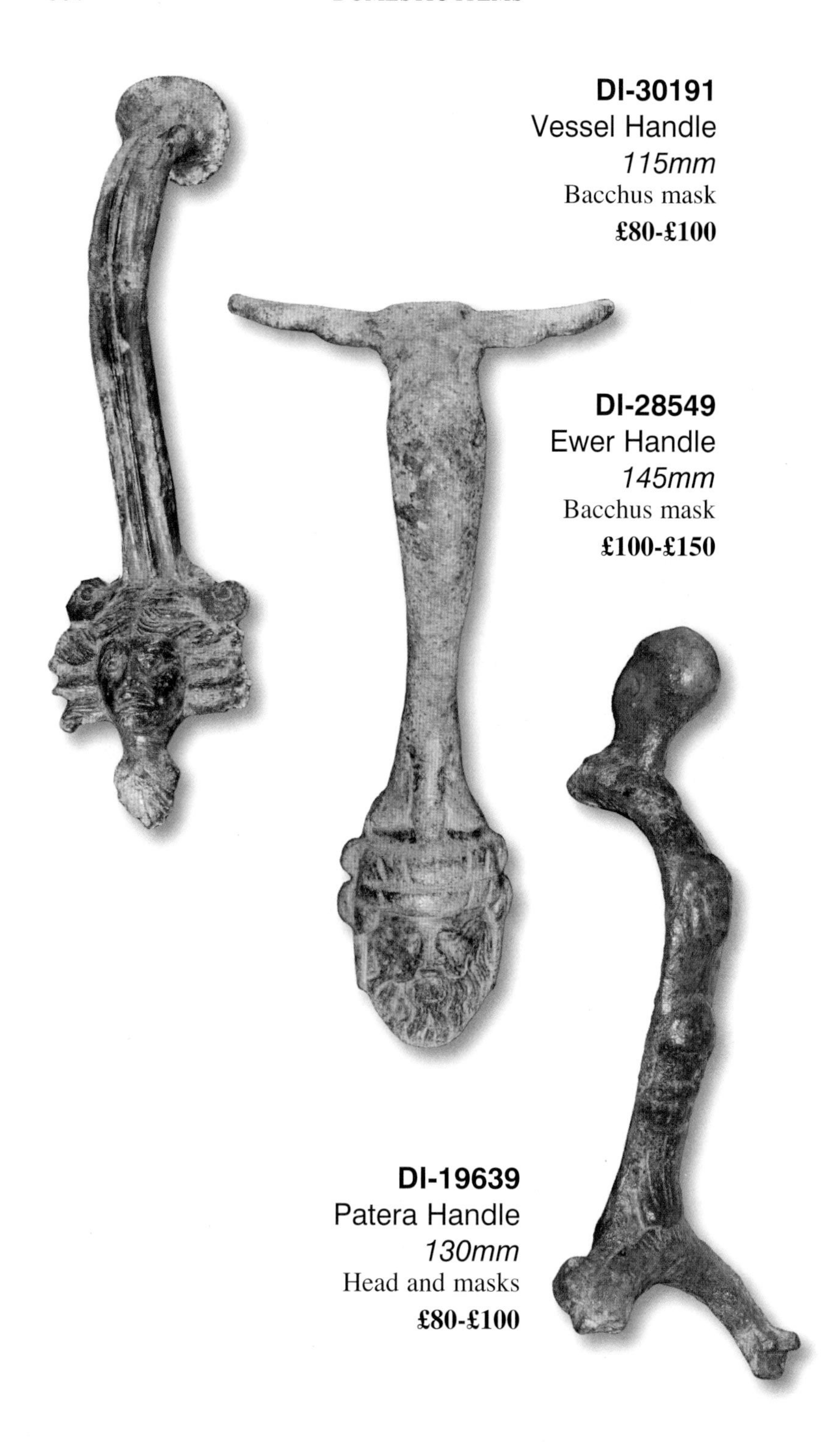

DI-30191
Vessel Handle
115mm
Bacchus mask
£80-£100

DI-28549
Ewer Handle
145mm
Bacchus mask
£100-£150

DI-19639
Patera Handle
130mm
Head and masks
£80-£100

DI-20989
Ewer Handle
83mm
Lion mask
£30-£40

DI-15282
Vessel
Handle
120mm
Two plates
with hooks
£100-£150

DI-17938
Jug Handle
52mm
Ram's head type
£80-£100

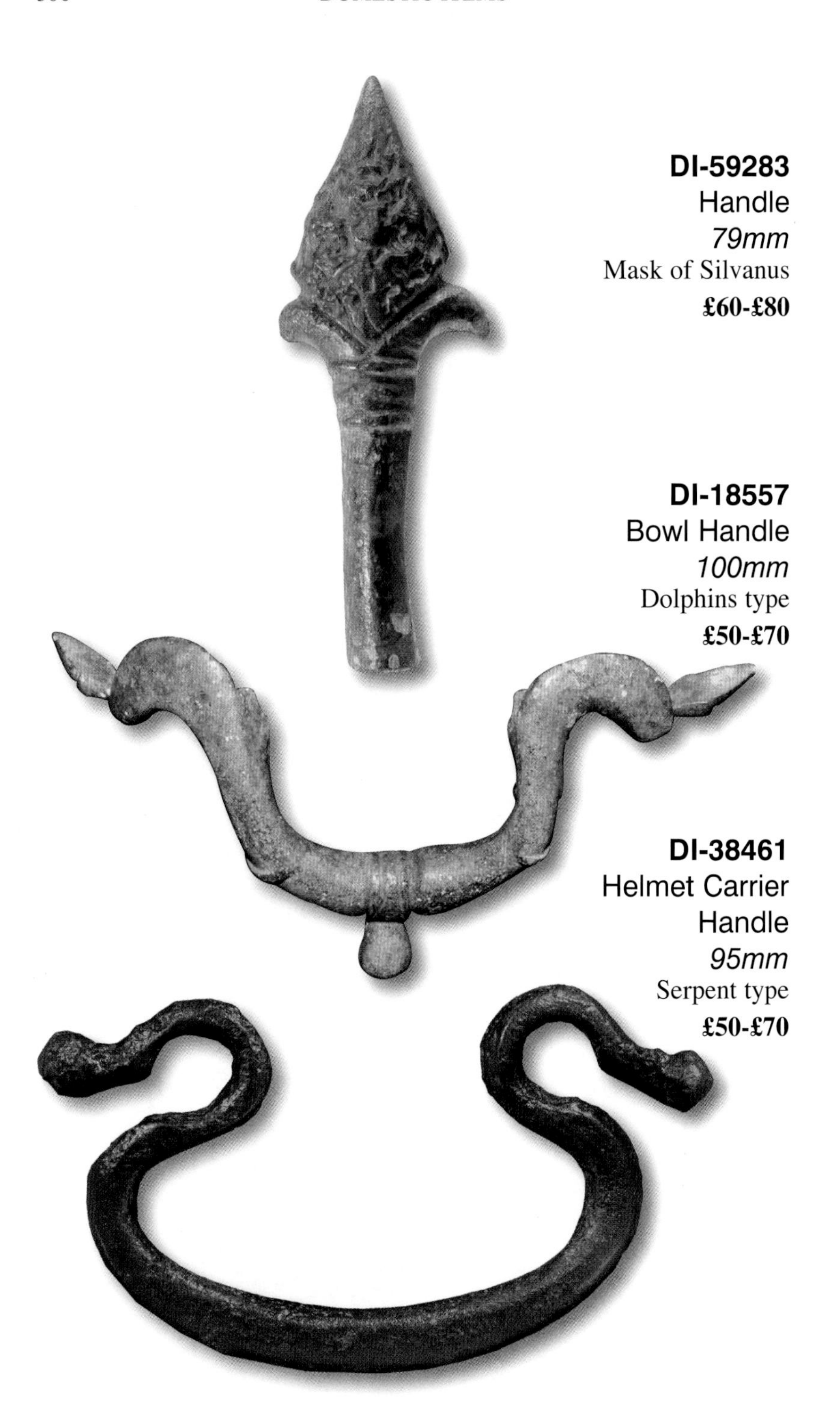

DI-59283
Handle
79mm
Mask of Silvanus
£60-£80

DI-18557
Bowl Handle
100mm
Dolphins type
£50-£70

DI-38461
Helmet Carrier
Handle
95mm
Serpent type
£50-£70

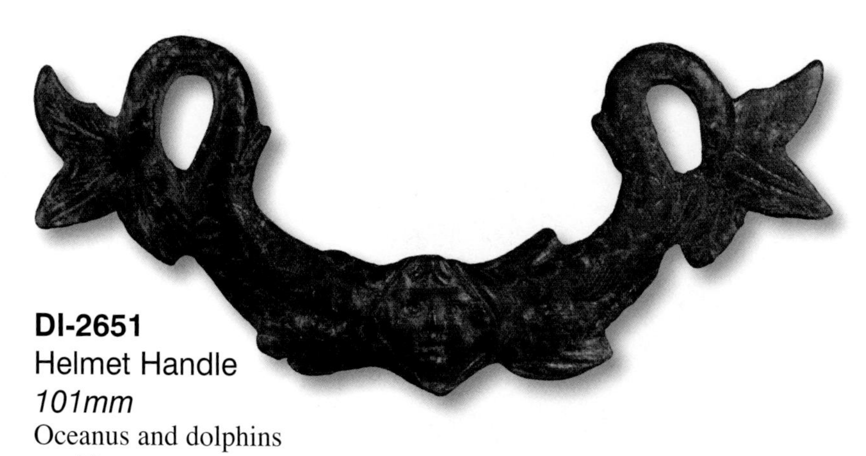

DI-2651
Helmet Handle
101mm
Oceanus and dolphins motif
£80-£100

DI-7639
Key Handle
90mm
Lion type
£200-£300

DI-2530
Key Handle
77mm
Lion type
£150-£200

DI-4738
Key
110mm
Lion type
£100-£150

DI-3274
Door Handle
200mm
Lion mask type
£1,500-£2,000

DI-40314
Handle with Inscription
68mm
Maker's mark '[.] ANSTEPHAPRO[DM]' (X Stephanus productavit me; 'S. produced me'?)
£120-£180

DI-54715
Casket Handle
37mm
Enamelled panels
£100-£150

DI-28753
Fitting
67mm
Lion's paw and harpy
£100-£150

DI-39065
Hasp
115mm
Female figure
£200-£300

DI-24147
Hasp Fitting
91mm
Dionysus type
£150-£200

DI-62890
Hasp
105mm
Male figure type
£100-£150

DI-64783
Hasp
115mm
Venus type
£120-£180

DI-2657
Lockplate Clasp
78mm
Athlete type
£100-£150

DI-43417
Wine
Flagon Lid
64mm
£80-£100

DI-32928
Vessel
Fragment
39mm
Erotic type
£80-£100

DI-19257
Wine Flagon
Section
38mm
Putto type
£60-£80

DI-3397
Vessel Lid
71mm
Medusa type
£80-£100

DI-38975
Figural Lock
Plate
96mm
£80-£100

DI-40319
Enamelled
Bronze
Votive Altar
28mm
Putto heads
£200-£300

DI-12924
Lead
Casket
Panel
385mm
Funerary
motifs
including
Dis, Charon
and Cerberus
£250-£350

DI-5115
Lead Panel
920mm
Ropework borders and vegetation supported by columns, a bird, a loosely draped standing figure and a crouching lion
£300-£400

DI-38739
Seal Box
25mm
With dog appliqué
£50-£70

DI-61639
Gilt Pyxis
56mm
With figures of the Gods
£300-£400

DI-63006
Pyxis with Hinged Lid
51mm
Ribbed surface, countersunk lid
£150-£200

DI-12217
Mirror
205mm
Masks of Mercury
£500-£700

DI-70775
Gilt Decorated Mirror
14cm
Running scrolled tendrils and openwork border
£500-£700

DI-34204
Hinged Mirror
140mm
Facing masks
£500-£700

DI-64702
Razor
52mm
Bronze handle with horse-heads
£150-£200

DI-65700
Folding Razor and Chain
21.5cm
Blade hinged at the lower end with spur
£100-£140

DI-56672
Cosmetic Chatelaine
130mm
Spoon, tweezers and spike
£100-£150

DI-38090
Strap End
87mm
Nail-cleaner type
£60-£80

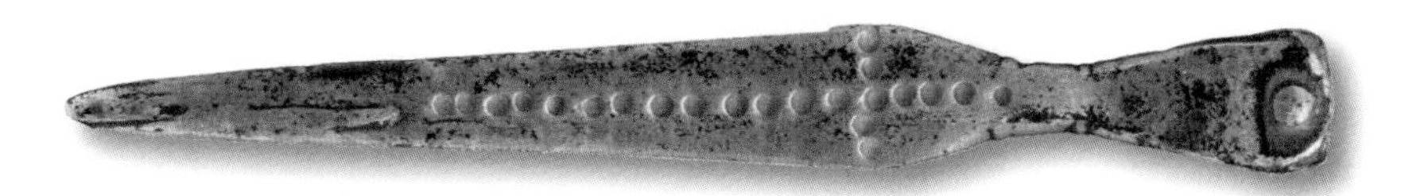

DI-42244
Strap End
75mm
Nail-cleaner type
£60-£80

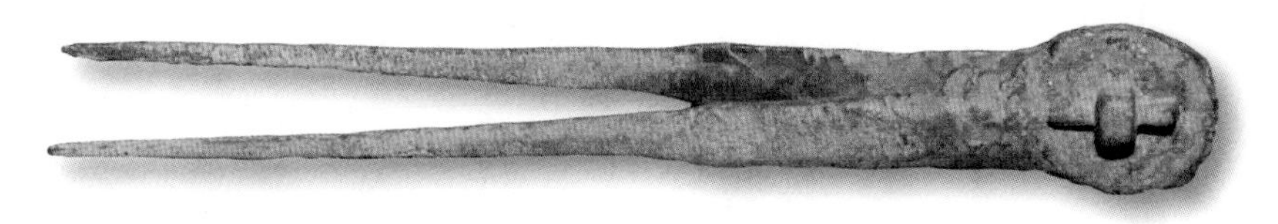

DI-13677
Dividers
98mm
£50-£80

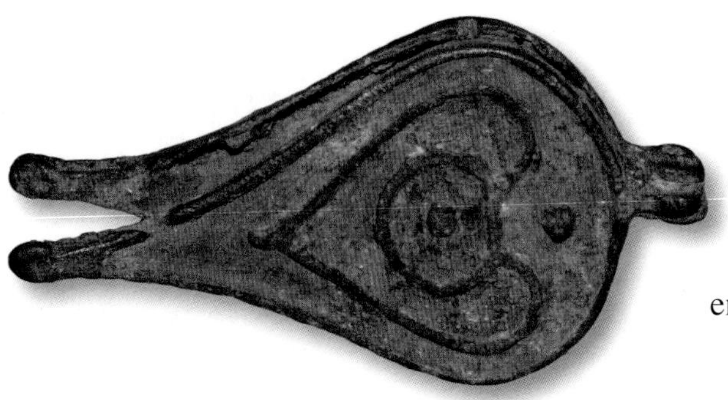

DI-66499
Enamelled
Seal Box
45mm
Heart-shaped
enamelled panel
£30-£40

DI-18101
Furniture
Foot
105mm
Putto type
From £1,000

DI-54325
Protome
100mm
Dionysus type
£1,500-£2,000

DI-11894
Protome
50mm
Griffin
£200-£300

DI-50519
Boar Fitting
76mm
Head on a plaque
£400-£600

DI-5704
Tripod
Campaign
Table Finial
82mm
Female bust
£200-£300

DI-31388
Campaign
Table
Terminal
105mm
Bacchus type
£200-£300

DI-7666
Tripod Campaign
Table Terminal
51mm
Bacchus type
£100-£150

DI-37283
Finial
34mm
Ram's head type
£100-£200

DI-18269
Lion Finial
57mm
With forepaws
extended
£100-£150

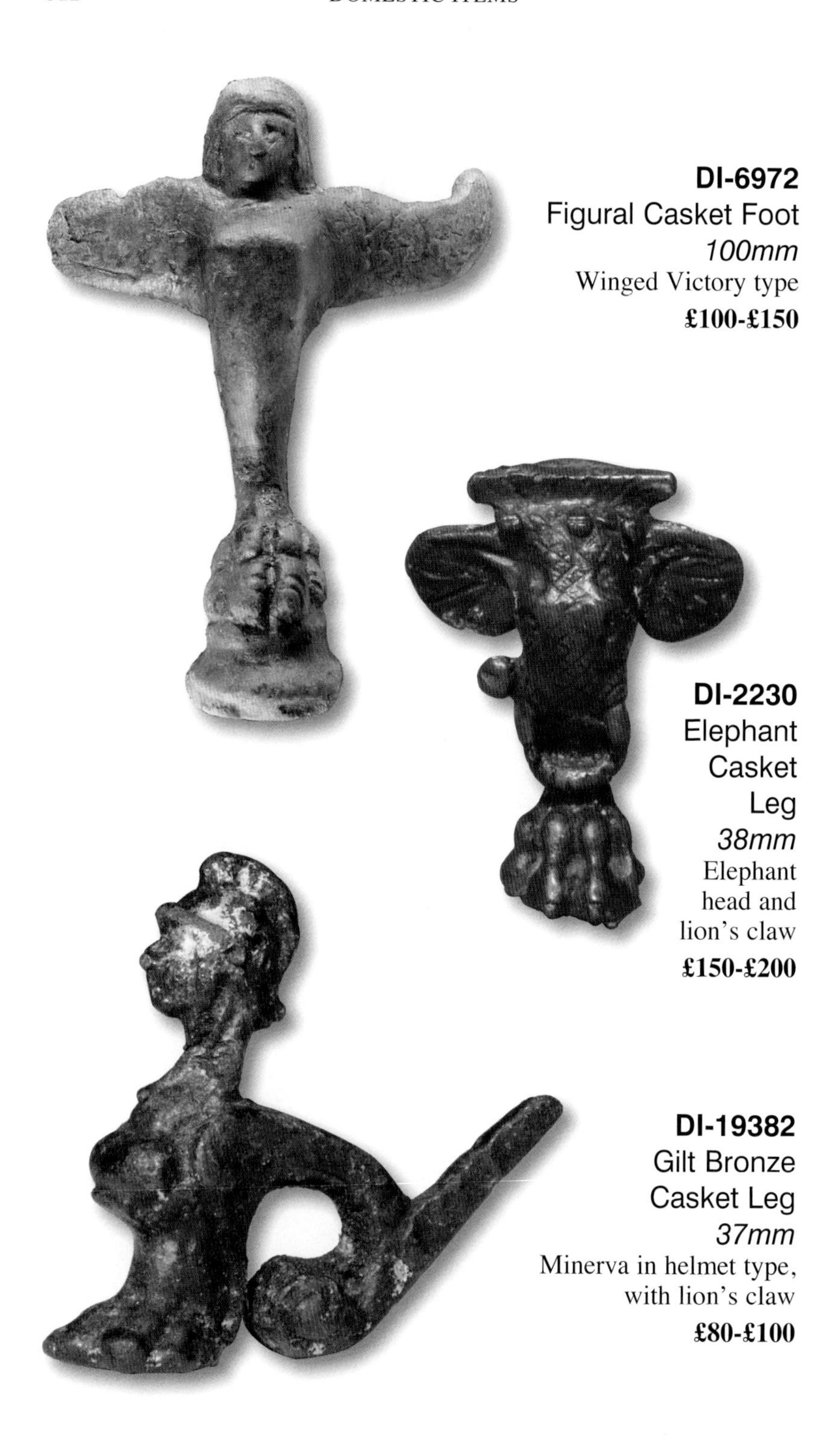

DI-6972
Figural Casket Foot
100mm
Winged Victory type
£100-£150

DI-2230
Elephant
Casket
Leg
38mm
Elephant
head and
lion's claw
£150-£200

DI-19382
Gilt Bronze
Casket Leg
37mm
Minerva in helmet type,
with lion's claw
£80-£100

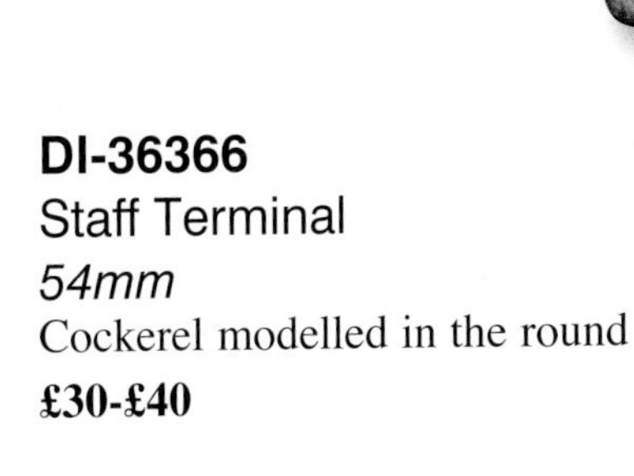

DI-36366
Staff Terminal
54mm
Cockerel modelled in the round
£30-£40

DI-6399
Stamp
38mm
Legion XII
£150-£200

DI-32160
Ingot Stamp
58mm
Military type, ‘LIM’, possibly for Limitanei, the military border-guards
£40-£60

DI-17775
Seal
260mm
Cockerel between two military standards
£120-£180

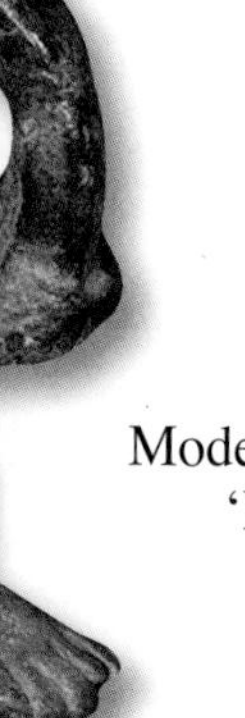

DI I-66376
Seal Matrix
52mm
Model human foot with retrograde 'FLX' legend for felix 'lucky'
£100-£150

DI-21820
Steelyard Weight
93mm
Masked Dionysus type
£800-£1,000

DI-2713
Steelyard Weight
135mm
Hercules type
£600-£800

DI-2925
Steelyard Weight
47mm
Bust of Emperor Vespasian
£500-£700

DI-38770
Military
Weight
67mm
Samped
'LEGIII'
and 'XVII'
£300-£400

DI-27176
Trade Weight
29mm
Busts of Marc Antony and Cleopatra
£150-£200

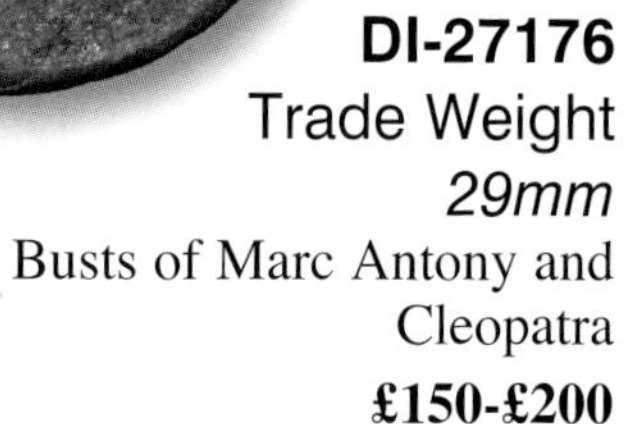

DI-17734
Steelyard Weight
73mm
Silenus type
£150-£200

DI-20327
Hercules Weight
32mm
Head of Hercules or a corresponding British god
£100-£150

DI-61710
Steelyard
Weight Pair
78mm
Minerva and
Victory busts
£80-£100

DI-71222
Miniature
Steelyard
Weight Group
22-25mm
Female busts
£80-£100

DI-47046
Steelyard Weight
33mm
Mercury bust
£60-£80

DI-30779
Weight
31mm
Sol Invictus type
£50-£70

DI-69853
Mason's Plumb Weight
50mm
£60-£80

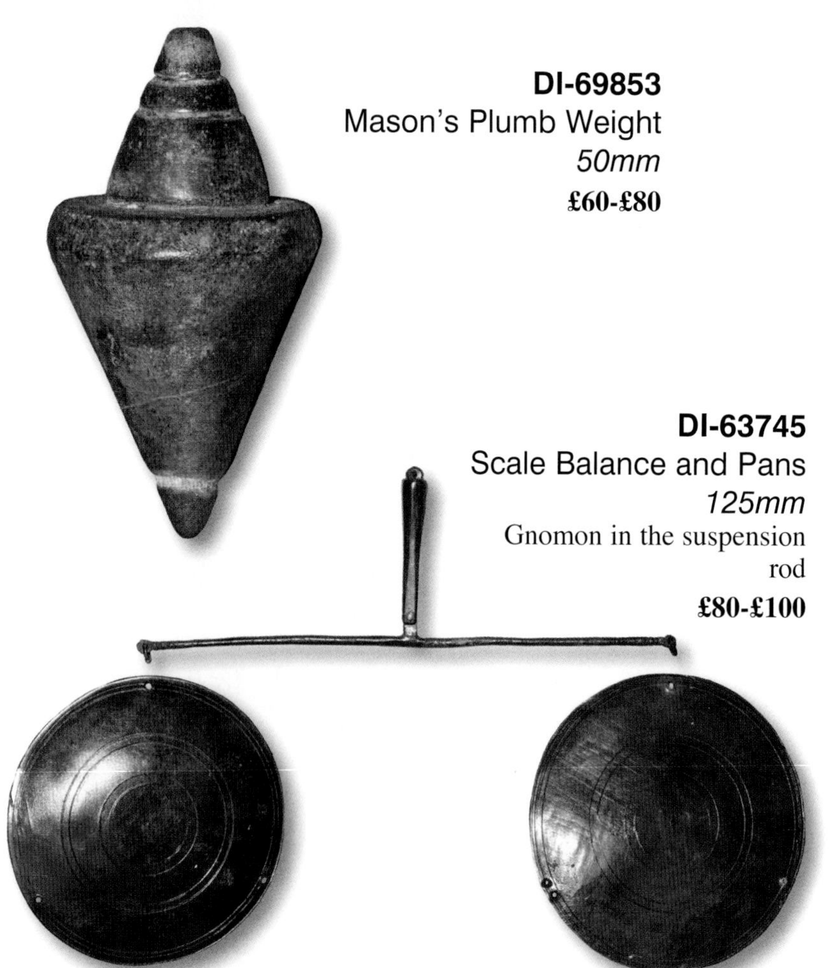

DI-63745
Scale Balance and Pans
125mm
Gnomon in the suspension rod
£80-£100

DI-62104

Steelyard

Balance and Pan

135mm

Notched gradations to three faces of the bar

£60-£80

DI-19217

Military Pouch

110mm

Bronze with ribbed outer surface

From £1,000

DI-64758

Military Diploma Section

150mm

Text on the reverse written at right-angles

From £500

DI-62179
Stylus with Eraser
130mm
Balustered handle and D-shaped eraser
£50-£70

DI-62178
Stylus with Eraser
135mm
Twisted shaft above the triangular eraser
£50-£70

DI-57296
1st Italic Legion Brick
195mm
Stamped 'LEG I ITAL' for Legio prima Italica '1st Italic Legion'
£150-£200

DI-44644
Stamped Block
195mm
Stamped with 'LEG I' twice (Legio Prima Italica)
£100-£150

DI-3532
Stamped Tile
180mm
Stamped 'LEG II ITA' (Legio II Italica)
£40-£60

DI-21571
Lead Brothel Token
54mm
£100-£150

DI-68349
Seal or Theatre Token
23mm
Image of a galley
£30-£40

DI-3736
Chi-Rho and Emperor Seal
19mm
Christogram to one face, imperial bust to the reverse
£50-£70

DI-38741
Counterfeiter's Denarius Mould Pair
26-28mm
Lead moulds for counterfeit coins of Caracalla or Geta
£40-£60

DI-35515
Dice Pair
17mm
£80-£100

DI-38970
Gaming Pieces
27-30mm
Sheep bones with lead fill
£80-£100

DI-67669
Bell with Face
40mm
Incised facial features
£60-£80

KNIVES & FITTINGS

Knives vary greatly in type in the Roman period. At the coarser end of the spectrum are butchery knives and everyday military equipment, characterised as sturdy in construction and perfectly functional. Daggers were also carried by civilians, often decorated and furnished with silver fittings. Table knives form a rarer class, again often decorated. The greatest craftsmanship often went into scalpels and other surgical tools which were elegantly designed for precise use.

Among the fittings associated with knives are the metal pommel, the bolster and the leather sheath or scabbard with metal elements such as the chape and suspension rings.

KA-16647
Gladius Pommel
40mm
Bust of Emperor Hadrian
£200-£300

KA-18741
Knife Pommel
39mm
Panther-heads type
£200-£300

KA-20278
Dagger Pommel
35mm
Gryphon-head type
£150-£200

KA-34559
Knife Pommel
30mm
Faun-head type
£80-£100

KA-18709
Knife Pommel
32mm
Panther-head type
£80-£100

KA-60775
Knife
Pommel
45mm
Eagle-head
type
£40-£60

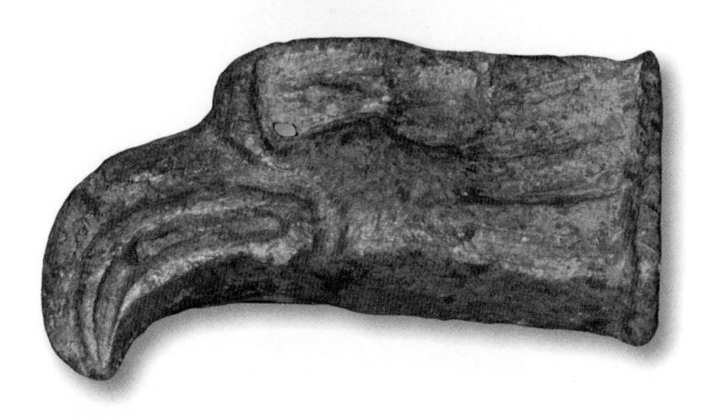

KA-11370
Knife Finial
38mm
Male bust type
£60-£80

KA-47053
Knife Guard
51mm
Socket with phallus to the centre, one arm a phallus and the other a fist in the 'fig' gesture
£60-£80

KA-33521
Knife Handle
36mm
Bust of Matrona
£100-£150

KA-64703
Knife Handle
70mm
Horse-head type
£150-£250

KA-38747
Knife Handle
67mm
Stylised bust
£80-£100

KA-21553
Aequitas Knife Handle
58mm
Aequitas (the personification of justice) standing with a cornucopia in the left arm and book (or scales) in the right
£80-£100

KA-18556
Knife handle
110mm
Running hound type
£60-£80

KA-22746
Folding Knife
71mm
Leaping lion or leopard type
£100-£150

KA-7421
Folding Knife
Handle
96mm
£100-£150

KA-62095
Folding
Knife
70mm
£120-£180

KA-51777
Knife
110mm
Lion's head handle
£150-£200

KA-46580
Knife
140mm
Ram's head type
£150-£200

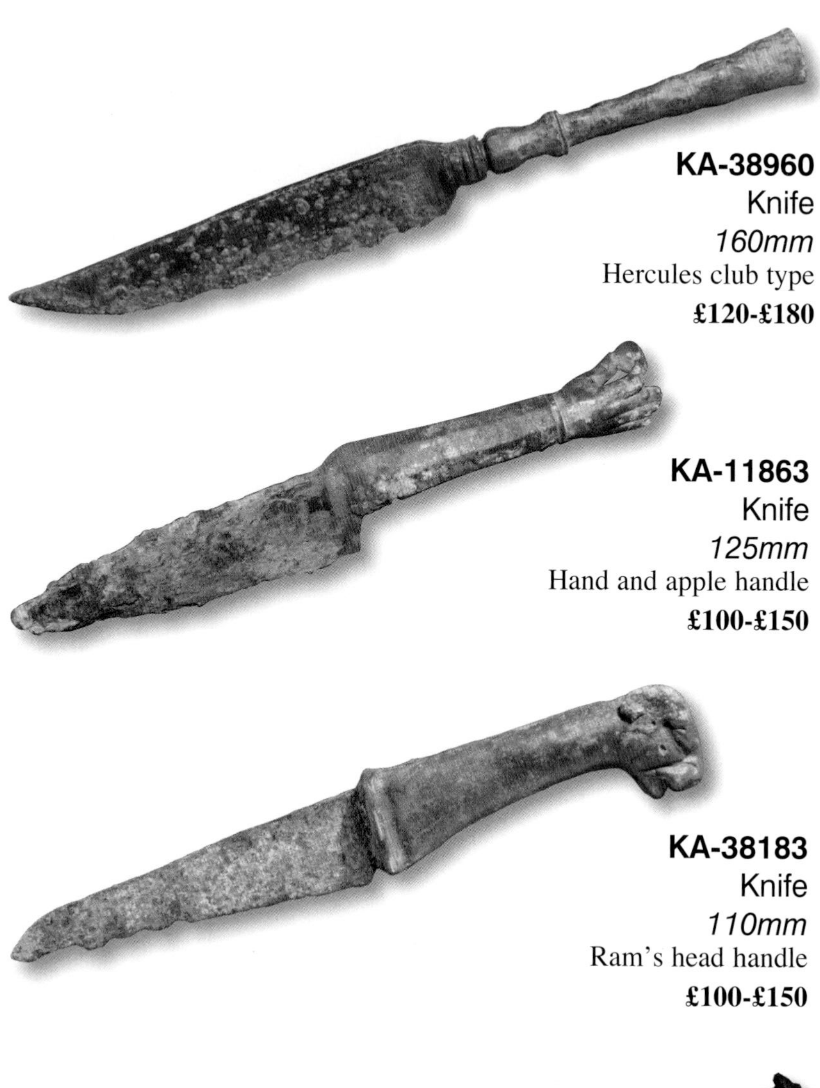

KA-38960
Knife
160mm
Hercules club type
£120-£180

KA-11863
Knife
125mm
Hand and apple handle
£100-£150

KA-38183
Knife
110mm
Ram's head handle
£100-£150

KA-20962
Knife
215mm
Ridged handle and pommel
£100-£150

KA-2398
Knife
122mm
Dolphin handle type
£100-£150

KA-20721
Knife
180mm
Tag fixed to the pommel
£100-£150

KA-60465
Knife
156mm
Linear decoration on the handle
£100-£150

KA-38257
Bronze Handled Knife
160mm
Ropework collar and octagonal-section grip
£100-£150

KA-13994
Gladius Blade
500mm overall
Parallel-sided
with short tang
£120-£180

KA-69465
Surgical Knife
125mm
£80-£100

KA-69466
Medical Scalpel
145mm
£80-£100

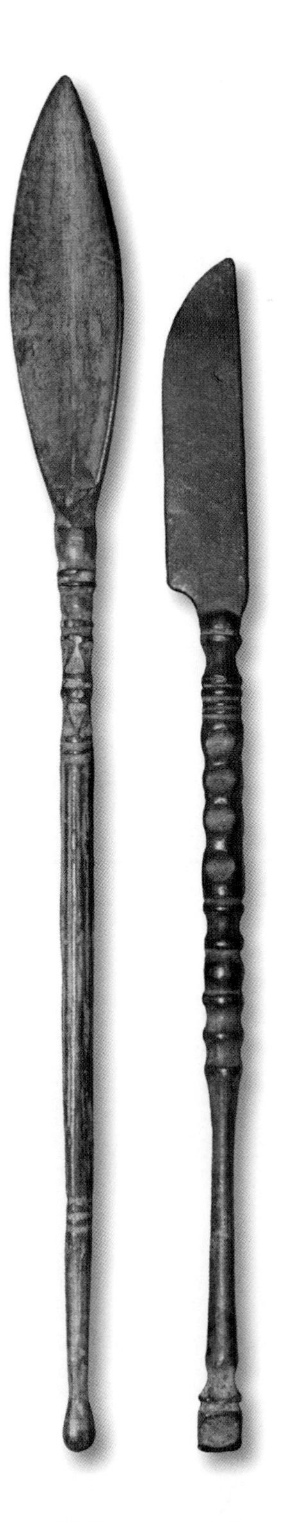

KA-64712
Medical
Instrument Pair
23cm-25cm
£80-£100

KA-40727
Caltrop
70mm
Bulb with four spikes
£80-£100

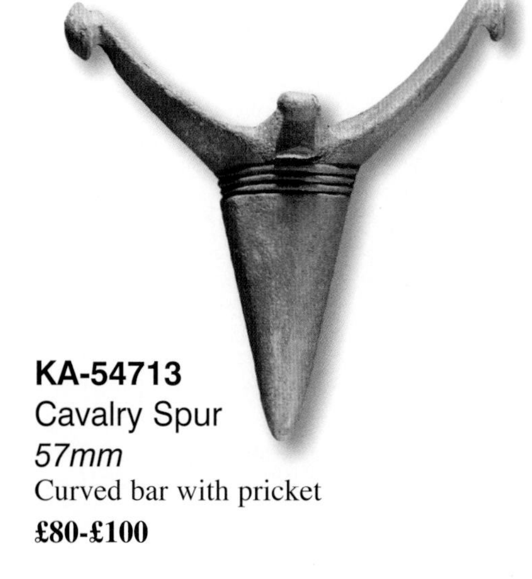

KA-54713
Cavalry Spur
57mm
Curved bar with pricket
£80-£100

CHARIOT FITTINGS

Roman chariots were opulent vehicles used mainly by the wealthy, government officials and the military. The frame was often studded with bronze or iron fittings, and repoussé plaques were placed on the visible surfaces for display purposes. The most prominent surfaces were provided with amuletic figures such as likenesses of gods and goddesses, as well as the protective gorgoneion mask.

Aside from the ornamental display elements, chariots also carried a number of loops and terrets which ensured that the reins and other straps did not become snared or tangled. These were often cast in bronze and decorative in form.

CF-11891
Chariot Fitting
66mm
Figure of Cupid with arms raised
£800-£1,000

CF-37516
Enamelled Chariot Fitting
120mm
Geometric enamelled designs
From £800

CF-5959
Chariot Fitting Pair
170mm
Two females with flowers and tendrils
£1,500-£2,000

CF-45581
Chariot
Fitting Pair
98mm
Isis-Fortuna
images
£1,000-£1,500

CF-54324
Chariot Fitting
140mm
Portrait of
Empress Faustina
From £2,500

CF-51755
Chariot Fitting
215mm
Bacchus with
vineleaves
£3,000-£4,000

CF-56116
Chariot Fitting
130mm
Hercules with lionskin mantle
From £1,000

CF-29535
Chariot Fitting
92mm
Female bust
£600-£800

CF-38959
Chariot Fitting
90mm
Male bust
£500-£700

CF-17731
Chariot Fitting
125mm
Head of Apollo
From £500

CF-6762
Chariot Fitting
98mm
Female bust
£150-£200

CF-52293
Chariot Fitting
94mm
Cupid with flowing hair and ropework collar
From £500

CF-23963
Chariot Strap Fitting
67mm
Scrolled tendrils
£100-£150

CF-3936
Chariot Fitting
110mm
Concentric rings
£100-£150

CF-45917
Chariot Fitting
165mm
Mask of Medusa on silver insert
From £500

CF-24150
Chariot
Fitting
67mm
Biga with Cupid
£150-£200

CF-23962
Chariot
Fitting
100mm
Scrolled
tendrils and
loop
£120-£180

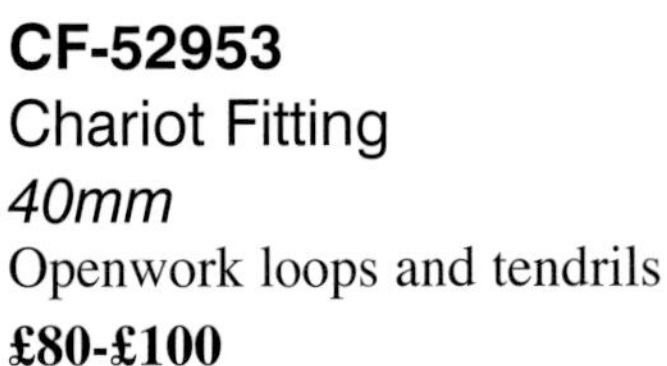

CF-52953
Chariot Fitting
40mm
Openwork loops and tendrils
£80-£100

CF-3682
Chariot Fitting
55mm
Four leaves type
£60-£80

CF I-5273
Chariot Fitting
100mm
Ridged domes
£50-£70

CF-40036
Chariot Fitting
36mm
Stud with four leaves
£20-£30

CF-3307
Chariot Reign Guide
68mm
Eagle head type
£100-£150

CF-2635
Chariot Fitting
57mm
Eagle head type
£100-£150

CF-52955
Bridle and Bit
145mm
£200-£300

CF-40895
Bridle Fitting Pair
140mm
Bronze rings and iron shafts
£100-£150

CF-40892
Bridle Fitting Pair
35-40mm
Volute scrolls and slots
£40-£60

CF-59445
Bridle Fitting
79mm
Volute scrolls and slot
£30-£40

CF-40893
Harness Fittings Suite
33-111mm
Two large discoid plaques and four studs with slots to the sides
£150-£200

CF-42206
Chariot Fitting
135mm
Javelin-wielding athlete with floral pillar

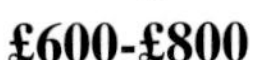

£600-£800

CF-21645
Harness Fitting
42mm
Openwork plaque with scrolls
£40-£60

CF-10393
Chariot Fitting
84mm
Actor's mask and inlaid eye
£400-£600

SJ-23964
Strap Distributor Roundel
105mm
Scrolled tendrils with spurs
£300-£400

SJ-7671
Strap Junction
89mm
Openwork tendrils and scrolls
£200-£300

SJ-27425
Strap Junction
90mm
Three'phalloi' around the central boss
£150-£200

SJ-48197
Chariot Strap Junction
65mm
Openwork scrolls and tendrils
£100-£150

SJ-48192
Chariot Strap
Junction
68mm
Openwork volute
scrolls and panels
£80-£100

SJ-48193
Chariot Strap
Junction
80mm
Openwork volute
scrolls and panels
£80-£100

SJ-48194
Strap Mount
45mm
Openwork panels
with lattice pattern
£60-£80

SJ-14826
Strap Junction
76mm
Scrolled tendrils and slots
£40-£60

SJ-28760
Strap Junction
54mm
Lion mask type
£60-£80

SJ-22791
Strap Junction
30mm
Lion mask type
£60-£80

STATUETTES

Statuettes and figurines, mainly made in bronze, began to become a common feature of life in Britain in the Roman period. Some were overtly religious in character depicting the gods and goddesses of the Roman pantheon – Jupiter, Mars, Venus, Fortuna, Victoria, Minerva and others. In certain cases the figures may have been used in temples for religious purposes while in others they appear to have been domestic, such as the lares and penates which protected the family home and hearth. Wealthier households could indulge their taste for ornament by having the figures' eyes inlaid in silver.

Another popular subject for such figurines is the gladiator or the legionary – often shown with drawn weapon held ready to strike. From such images the details of clothing and military equipment can be deduced as well as the use of shields, swords and other weaponry.

Animals and birds figure large among the non-human subjects. Some animals were regarded as sacred to a specific deity while others were hunted or reared for food. It is likely that many such figures were used in temples as part of religious observances.

FS-3075
Stone Altar
410mm
MARTI SANC / TO SACRVM / C(aius) IVL(ius) ANTO / NINVS MIL(es) / [le]G(ionis) XI CL(audiae) / [e] X VOTO POSV / VIT (Sacred to Mars Sanctus (The Holy), Gaius IuliusAntoninus, soldier in the 11th Claudian legion, set (this) up according to (his) vow)
From £1,000

FS-10049
Head of Cupid
270mm
From £10,000

FS-13042
Head of a Goddess
280mm
From £5,000

FS-30093
Stele with Seated Figures
650mm
Inscribed personal name
'SCRIBONIUS CIMBER (...)'
From £1,000

FS-57449
Head of Gaius Caesar
170mm
From £5,000

FS-12549
Urn Figurine Fragment
180mm
Lower legs and base of the urn
From £1,000

FS-2396
Head of Vitellius
79mm
Three-quarter view
£400-£600

FS-4762
Frieze Fragment
150mm
Secutor with gladius attacked by lions
£400-£600

FS-4763
Frieze Fragment
130mm
Gladiators fighting
£300-£400

FS-6078
Jupiter Figurine
128mm
Standing with arm raised
£800-£1,000

FS-8807
Jupiter Figurine
114mm
Standing with lightning bolt
£500-£700

FS-2029
Jupiter Statuette
93mm
Standing with patera
£500-£700

FS-3078
Jupiter Figurine
66mm
Standing with lightning bolt
£400-£600

FS-31778
Jupiter Statuette
70mm
Standing with cloak and lightning bolt
£300-£400

FS-6722
Jupiter Figurine
78mm
Standing with cloak and lightning bolt
£200-£300

FS-22779
Jupiter Statuette
110mm
Standing with arm extended
£300-£400

FS-18198
Jupiter Statuette
67mm
Standing with arms to the sides
£80-£100

FS-28751
Jupiter
Statuette
96mm
Standing with
left arm raised
£100-£150

FS-22793
Jupiter Statuette
59mm
Standing with left arm raised
£100-£150

FS-35317
Head of Jupiter
56mm
Bearded and with dressed hair
£200-£300

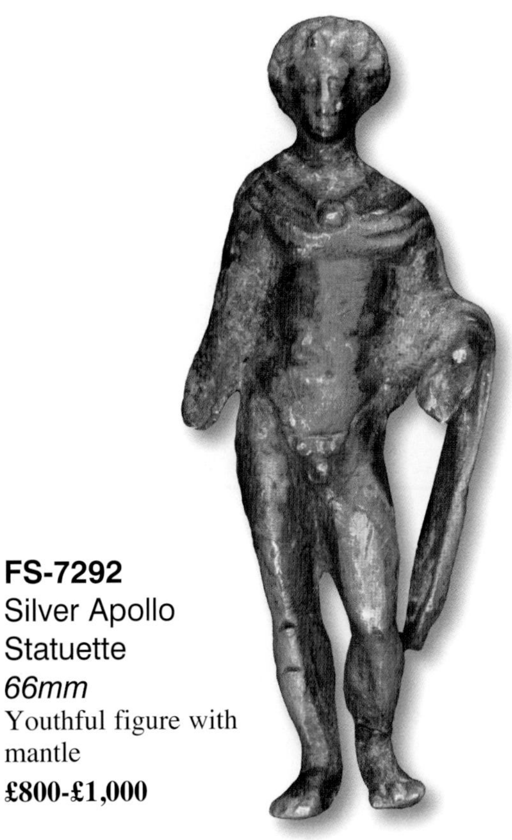

FS-7292
Silver Apollo Statuette
66mm
Youthful figure with mantle
£800-£1,000

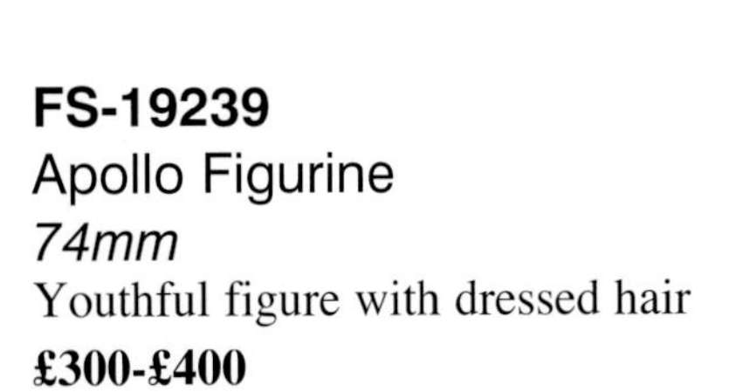

FS-19239
Apollo Figurine
74mm
Youthful figure with dressed hair
£300-£400

FS-43625
Head of Apollo
38mm
Radiate crown to the brow
£150-£200

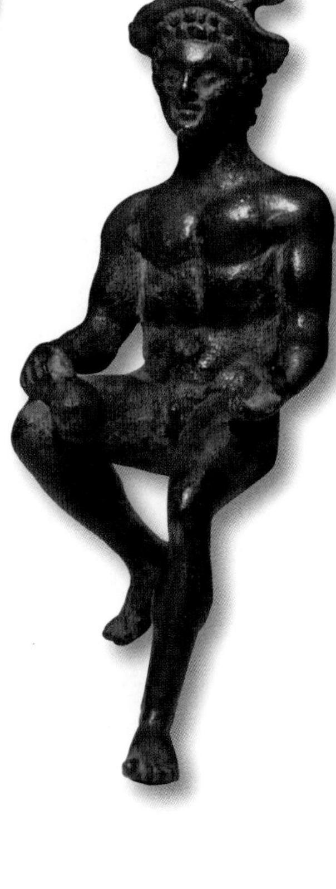

FS-45098
Seated Mercury Statuette
110mm
With winged petasos
From £1,000

FS-24883
Apollo Figurine
62mm
Youthful figure with mantle
£60-£80

FS-11893
Figure of Mercury
85mm
With winged petasos
From £1,000

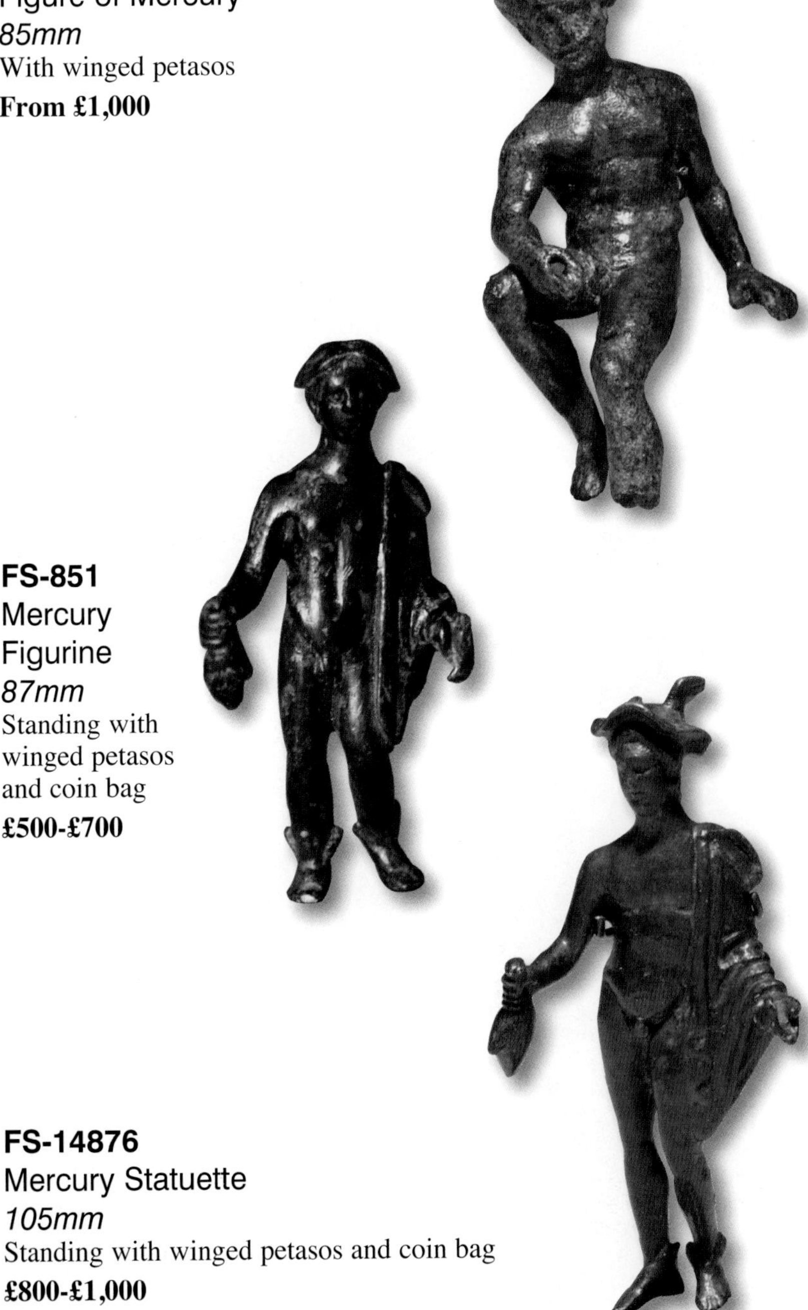

FS-851
Mercury
Figurine
87mm
Standing with
winged petasos
and coin bag
£500-£700

FS-14876
Mercury Statuette
105mm
Standing with winged petasos and coin bag
£800-£1,000

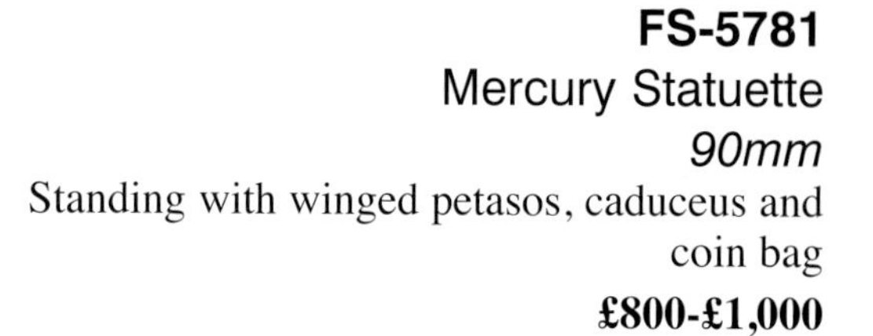

FS-5781

Mercury Statuette

90mm

Standing with winged petasos, caduceus and coin bag

£800-£1,000

FS-57623

Mercury Statuette

75mm

Standing with winged petasos and mantle

£300-£400

FS-61893

Mercury Statuette with Votive Bracelet

88mm

Standing with winged petasos, caduceus and coin bag, votive bracelet wound around the figure

£300-£400

FS-13673
Mercury Statuette
66mm
With coin bag and mantle
£250-£350

FS-29096
Mercury
Statuette
99mm
On socle base,
winged
£300-£400

FS-19238
Mercury Figurine
84mm
With winged petasos and caduceus
£250-£350

FS-40062
Mercury Statuette
63mm
With winged petasos and mantle
£200-£300

FS-12804
Mercury Figurine
63mm
With winged petasos and mantle
£200-£300

FS-828
Mercury Figurine
70mm
With winged petasos and mantle
£150-£200

FS-57632
Mercury Statuette
56mm
With mantle and coin bag
£150-£200

FS-60526
Mercury
Statuette
50mm
Seated
wearing
mantle
£150-£200

FS-52832
Mercury Statuette
50mm
With caduceus and coin bag
£150-£200

FS-9846
Mercury Figurine
65mm
With petasos, mantle and coin bag
£150-£200

FS-33978
Mercury Statuette
66mm
With caduceus and mantle
£150-£200

FS-18199
Mercury Statuette
53mm
With caduceus and coin bag
£120-£180

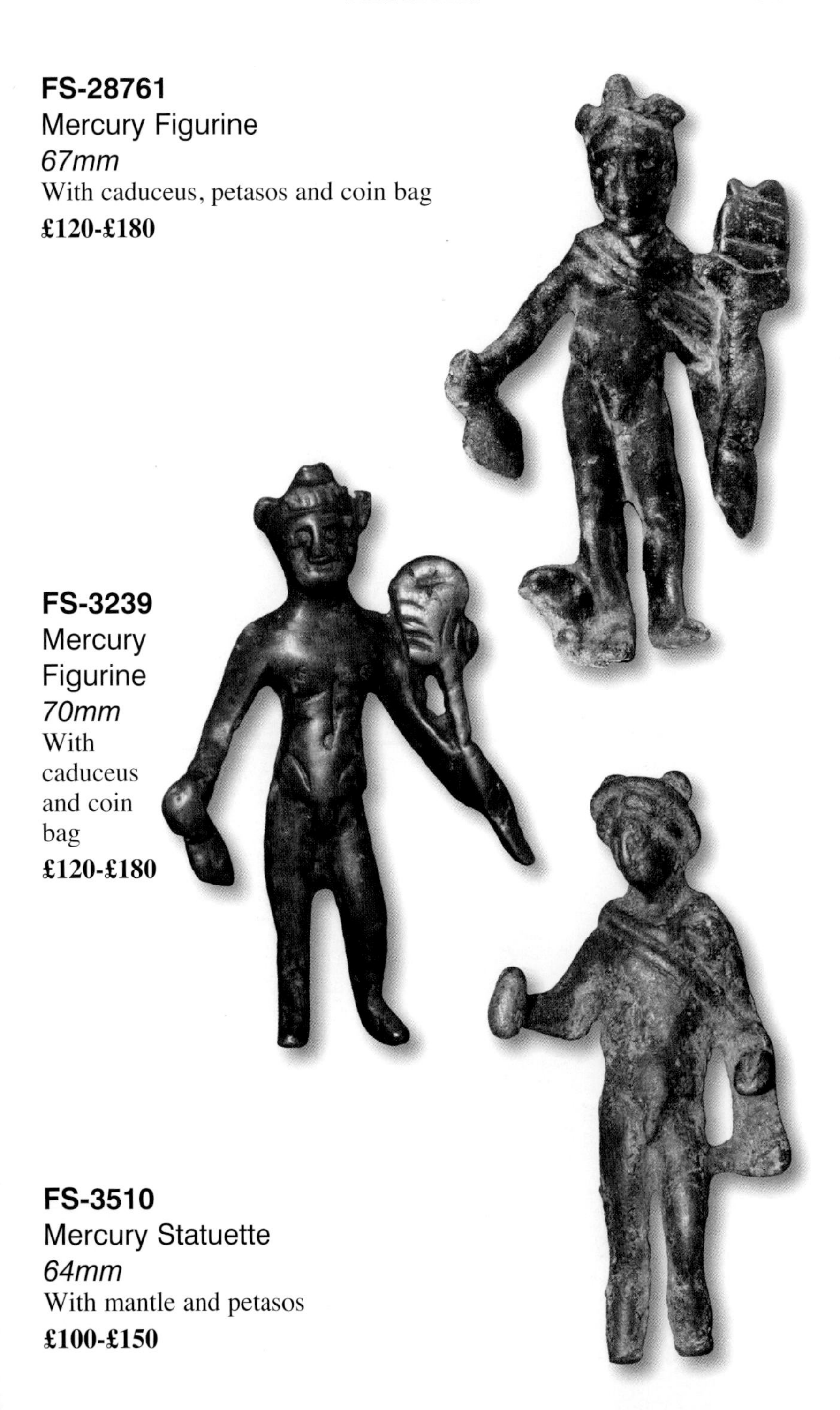

FS-28761
Mercury Figurine
67mm
With caduceus, petasos and coin bag
£120-£180

FS-3239
Mercury Figurine
70mm
With caduceus and coin bag
£120-£180

FS-3510
Mercury Statuette
64mm
With mantle and petasos
£100-£150

FS-2302
Mercury Statuette
46mm
With caduceus and coin bag
£80-£100

FS-9634
Mercury
Figurine
71mm
With
petasos and
coin bag
£60-£80

FS-16185
Mercury Statuette
63mm
With caduceus and coin bag
£80-£100

FS-18201
Mercury Statuette
41mm
With caduceus and petasos
£60-£80

FS-1979
Eros with Cornucopia Statuette
268mm
On square base with bun feet
From £10,000

FS-51115
Cupid Statuette
330mm
With right arm raised
£800-£1,000

FS-57261
Eros Statuette
90mm
With cornucopia
£600-£800

FS-110
Cupid
Figurine
70mm
Winged
figure with
raised arm
£500-£700

FS-57262
Eros Balsamarium
81mm
Hollow vessel shaped in the likeness
of the god
£600-£800

FS-57633
Eros Statuette
87mm
Standing on a columnar base
£400-£600

FS-2616
Venus
Statuette
133mm
Standing nude
with one hand
dressing the
hair
£400-£600

FS-12892
Putto Statuette
50mm
Standing nude
£300-£400

FS-11606
Dancing Putto Figurine
56mm
With leg raised
£200-£300

FS-22872
Putto Statuette
42mm
Sitting nude with arms raised
£300-£400

FS-31777
Putto Statuette
67mm
Standing nude
£200-£300

FS-56674
Putto Figurine
33mm
Seated, with arm raised
£120-£180

FS-7420
Putto
Statuette
51mm
Advancing
pose with arm
extended
£80-£100

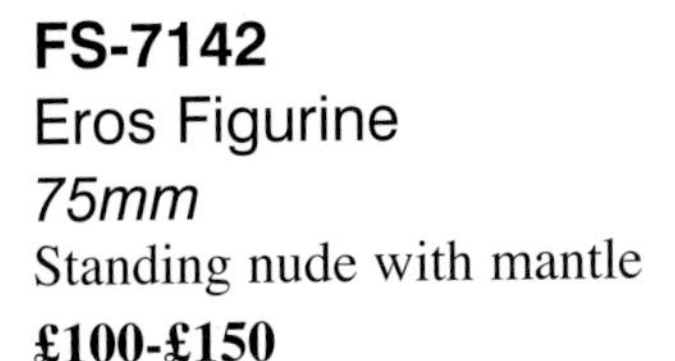

FS-7142
Eros Figurine
75mm
Standing nude with mantle
£100-£150

FS-57613
Mars Statuette
120mm
Helmeted and cloaked
From £1,000

FS-26583
Mars
Statuette
105mm
Helmeted
with right
arm raised
£500-£700

FS-64790
Mars Statuette
100mm
Helmeted and armoured
£500-£700

FS-5391
Bust of Mars
86mm
On socle base
£200-£300

FS-42451
Bust of Bacchus
190mm
With silver-inlaid eyes
£500-£700

FS-11796
Bacchus and Maenad Pole Finial
160mm
Two faces in opposite directions
From £500

FS-3075
Dionysus Figurine
85mm
On socle base
£300-£400

FS-35318
Bacchus Statuette
105mm
Standing with dressed hair
£300-£400

FS-7341
Dionysus Statuette
57mm
With cup and mantle
£150-£200

FS-46568
Asclepius Statuette
105mm
With loosely draped robe
From £2,000

FS-7079
Asculapius Statuette
93mm
With loosely draped robe
£400-£600

FS-25404
Atlas Statuette
99mm
Head bent forward to support the world
£400-£600

FS-51756
River God Statuette
94mm
Personification of the River Nile
£2,000-£3,000

FS-42192
Figurine of the God Nilus
81mm
The personification of the River Nile
500-£700

FS-45100
Attis Statuette
89mm
Helmeted with cuirass
£700-£900

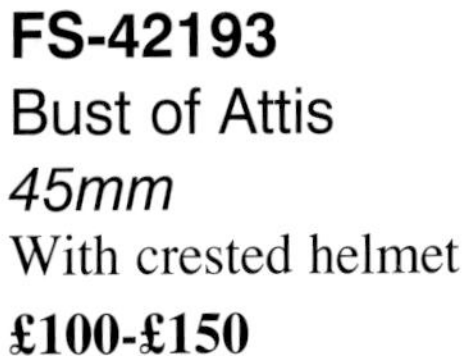

FS-42193
Bust of Attis
45mm
With crested helmet
£100-£150

FS-51760
Priapus Figurine
77mm
With extended phallus
£500-£700

FS-24095
Priapus Statuette
105mm
With extended arm and phallus
£400-£600

FS-45096
Priapus Figurine
68mm
With food balanced on the phallus
£300-£400

FS-4656
Priapus
Statuette
55mm
With phallus
beneath the
cloak
£150-£200

FS-47729
Head of Faunus
41mm
Bearded with horns
£150-£200

FS-3946
Pan Carrying Dionysus Figurine
130mm
£500-£800

FS-3403
Head of Pan
65mm
Bearded with horns to the brow
£200-£300

FS-3935
Bust of Serapis
90mm
With modius on the head
£150-£200

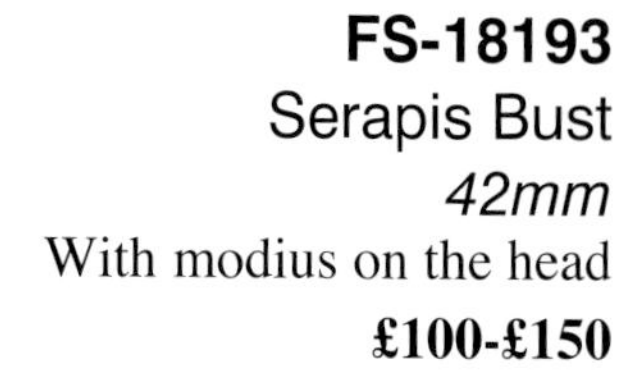

FS-18193
Serapis Bust
42mm
With modius on the head
£100-£150

FS-31460
Serapis Bust
47mm
With modius
on the head
£150-£200

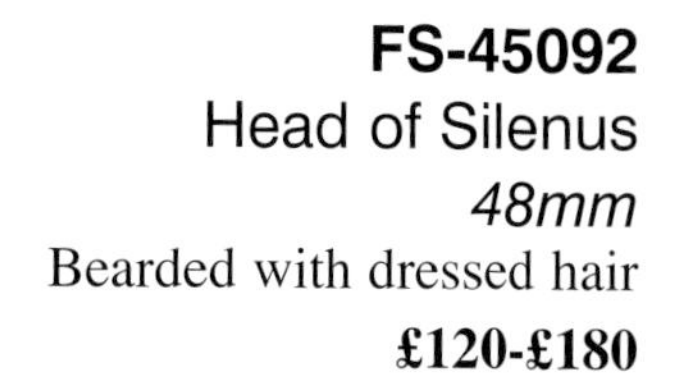

FS-45092
Head of Silenus
48mm
Bearded with dressed hair
£120-£180

FS-10269

Satyr Figurine

98mm

Legs bent beneath the body

£600-£800

FS-26914

Dioscuros Statuette

97mm

On socle base with thunderbolt

£400-£600

FS-40208

Harpocrates Statuette

79mm

With finger pressed to his lips

£200-£300

FS-63735
Silver Hercules Statuette
62mm
With lionskin mantle and club
£800-£1,000

FS-61908
Hercules and Antaeus Statuette
77mm
With lionsklin mantle and club on a rectangular plinth base
£800-£1,000

FS-9779

Bust of the Young Hercules

80mm

Bearded and youthful

£800-£1,000

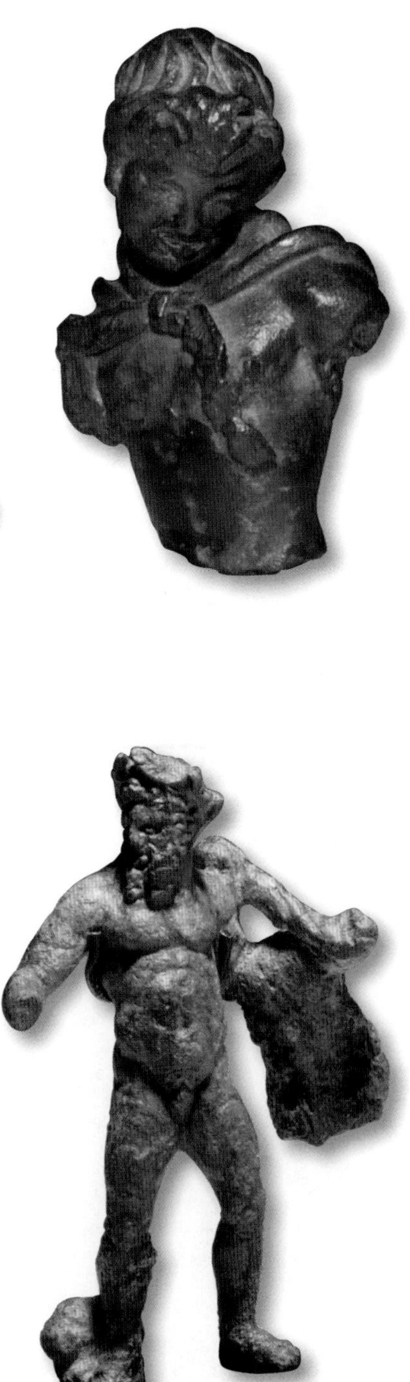

FS-11278

Hercules Statuette

110mm

With lionskin mantle and club

£600-£800

FS-52828

Hercules Bibax Statuette

81mm

With lionskin mantle

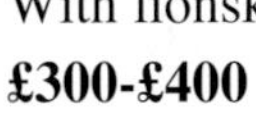

£300-£400

FS-57622
Hercules Bibax Statuette
78mm
With mantle and club, drinking from a wineskin
£400-£600

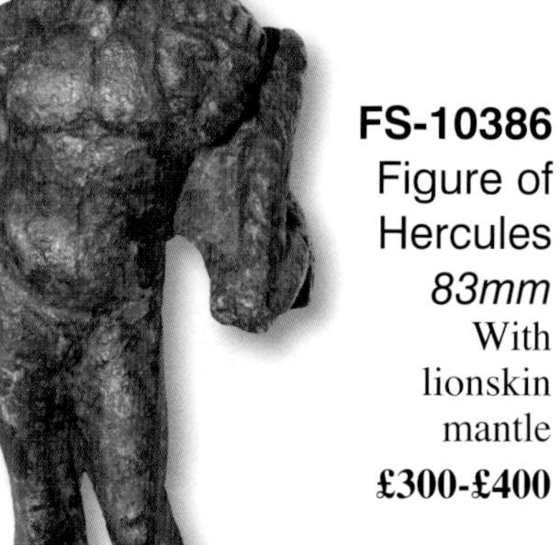

FS-10386
Figure of Hercules
83mm
With lionskin mantle
£300-£400

FS-57815
Hercules Statuette
90mm
With lionskin mantle and club
£200-£300

FS-2531
Hercules Statuette
87mm
With lionskin mantle and club
£300-£400

FS-50502
Bust of Hercules
57mm
Bearded with lionskin mantle
£200-£300

FS-54351
Young Hercules Statuette
78mm
Youthful figure with lionskin mantle
£300-£400

FS-12742
Hercules Statuette
62mm
With club in left hand
£200-£300

FS-38743
Hercules
Figurine
79mm
With arms
extended
£100-£150

FS-23459
Infant Hercules Figurine
53mm
Strangling snakes while still a
baby
£120-£180

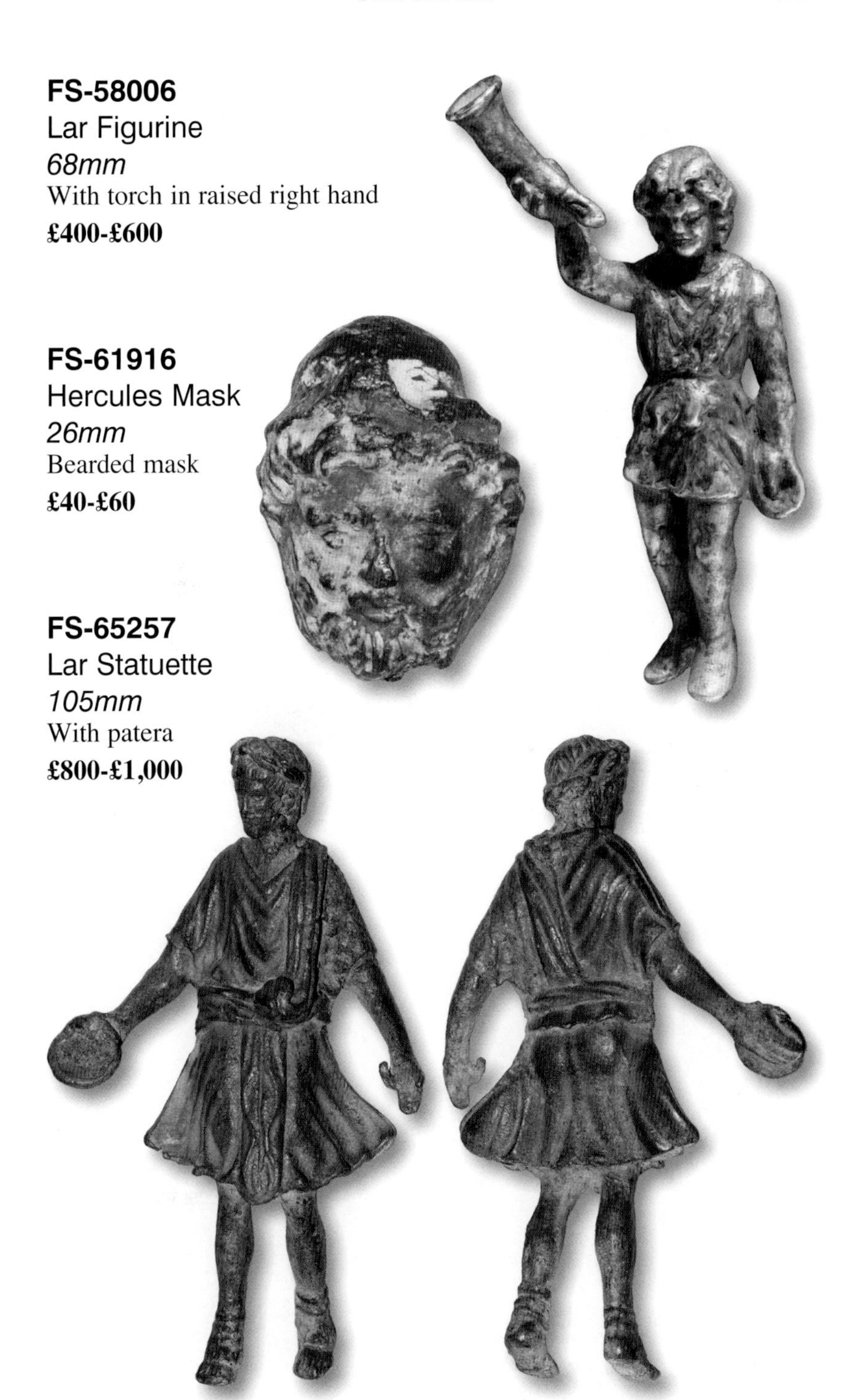

FS-58006
Lar Figurine
68mm
With torch in raised right hand
£400-£600

FS-61916
Hercules Mask
26mm
Bearded mask
£40-£60

FS-65257
Lar Statuette
105mm
With patera
£800-£1,000

FS-57520
Lar Statuette
125mm
With torch in raised right hand
£600-£800

FS-5905
Lar Figurine
110mm
Standing robed
£200-£300

FS-60459
Bound Captive Statuette
36mm
Rope round the neck wrists and ankles
£200-£300

FS-61357
Silver Bound Captive Statuette
53mm
Rope round the neck wrists and ankles
£300-£400

FS-18321
Bound Captive Figurine
34mm
Rope round the neck wrists and ankles
£200-£300

FS-46115
Bound Captive Figurine
93mm
Rope round the raised wrists
£300-£400

FS-2395
Gladiator Figurine
138mm
With spear and cloak
From £1,000

FS-2220
Gladiator Figurine
46mm
Retiarius gladiator armed with a net and trident
From £1,000

FS-51757
Gladiator Figurine
70mm
Murmillo with shield, helmet and short sword
From £1,000

FS-18309
Gladiator Figurine
51mm
Murmillo with short sword and helmet
From £600

FS-34598
Gladiator Figurine
77mm
Murmillo with helmet, shield and short sword
£250-£350

FS-51481
Gladiator Figurine
57mm
Standing with plumed helmet
£80-£100

FS-48132
Thraex Gladiator Figurine
35mm
With Thracian helmet
£80-£100

FS-36813
Lead Gladiators Figurine
70mm
Swordsmen clashing on a baseline
£100-£150

FS-6564
Lead Gladiators Figurine
61mm
Advancing on a baseline with shields to the front
£100-£150

FS-31441
Lead Gladiator Figurine
46mm
Lead souvenir from the gladiatorial games
£40-£60

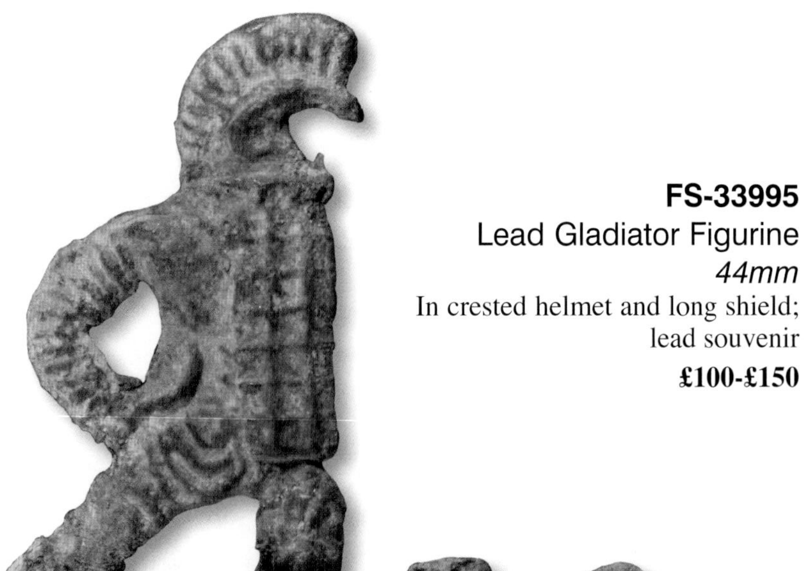

FS-33995
Lead Gladiator Figurine
44mm
In crested helmet and long shield; lead souvenir
£100-£150

FS-57619
Acrobat Statuette
90mm
In loincloth
£500-£700

FS-19284
Philosopher Figurine
39mm
In loose robe with left hand extended
£300-£400

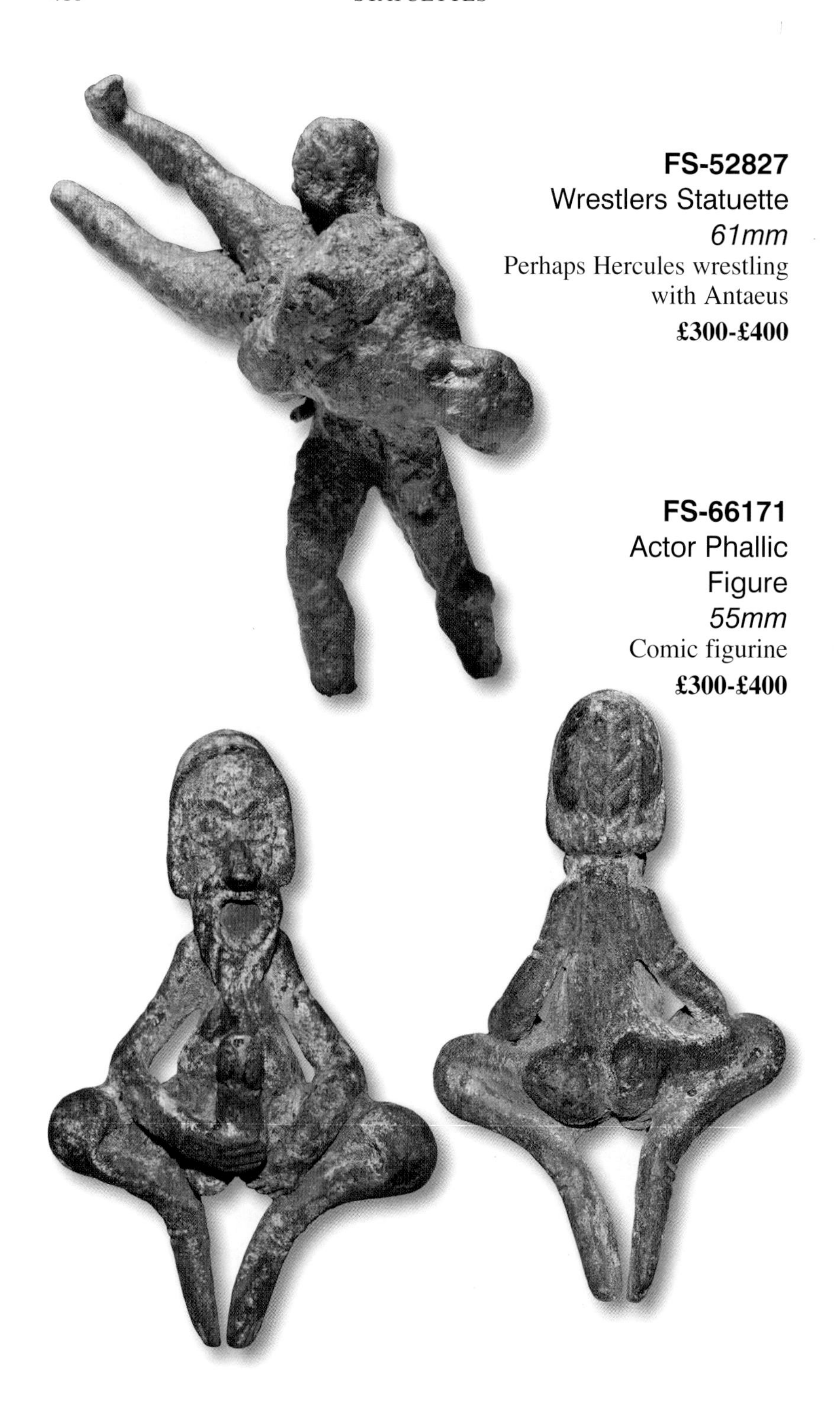

FS-52827
Wrestlers Statuette
61mm
Perhaps Hercules wrestling with Antaeus
£300-£400

FS-66171
Actor Phallic Figure
55mm
Comic figurine
£300-£400

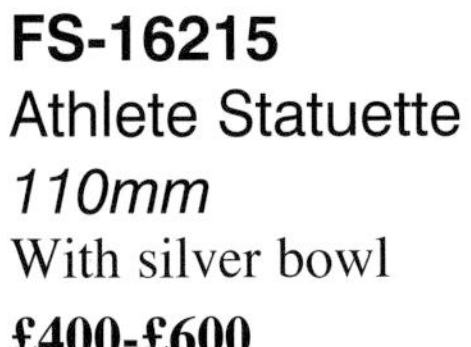

FS-16215
Athlete Statuette
110mm
With silver bowl
£400-£600

FS-6721
Banqueteer
Statuette
59mm
Reclining figure on
couch
£200-£300

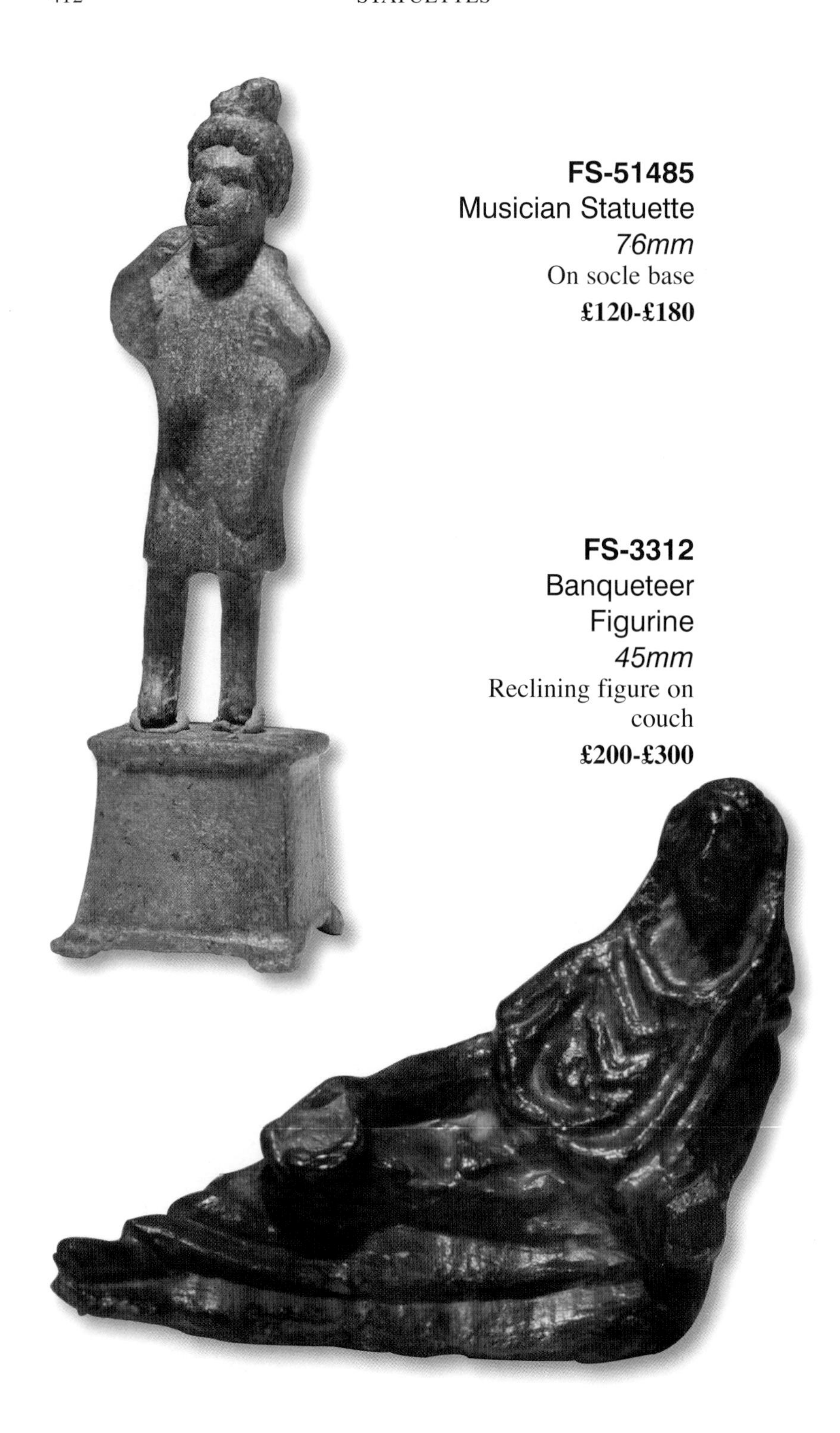

FS-51485
Musician Statuette
76mm
On socle base
£120-£180

FS-3312
Banqueteer
Figurine
45mm
Reclining figure on
couch
£200-£300

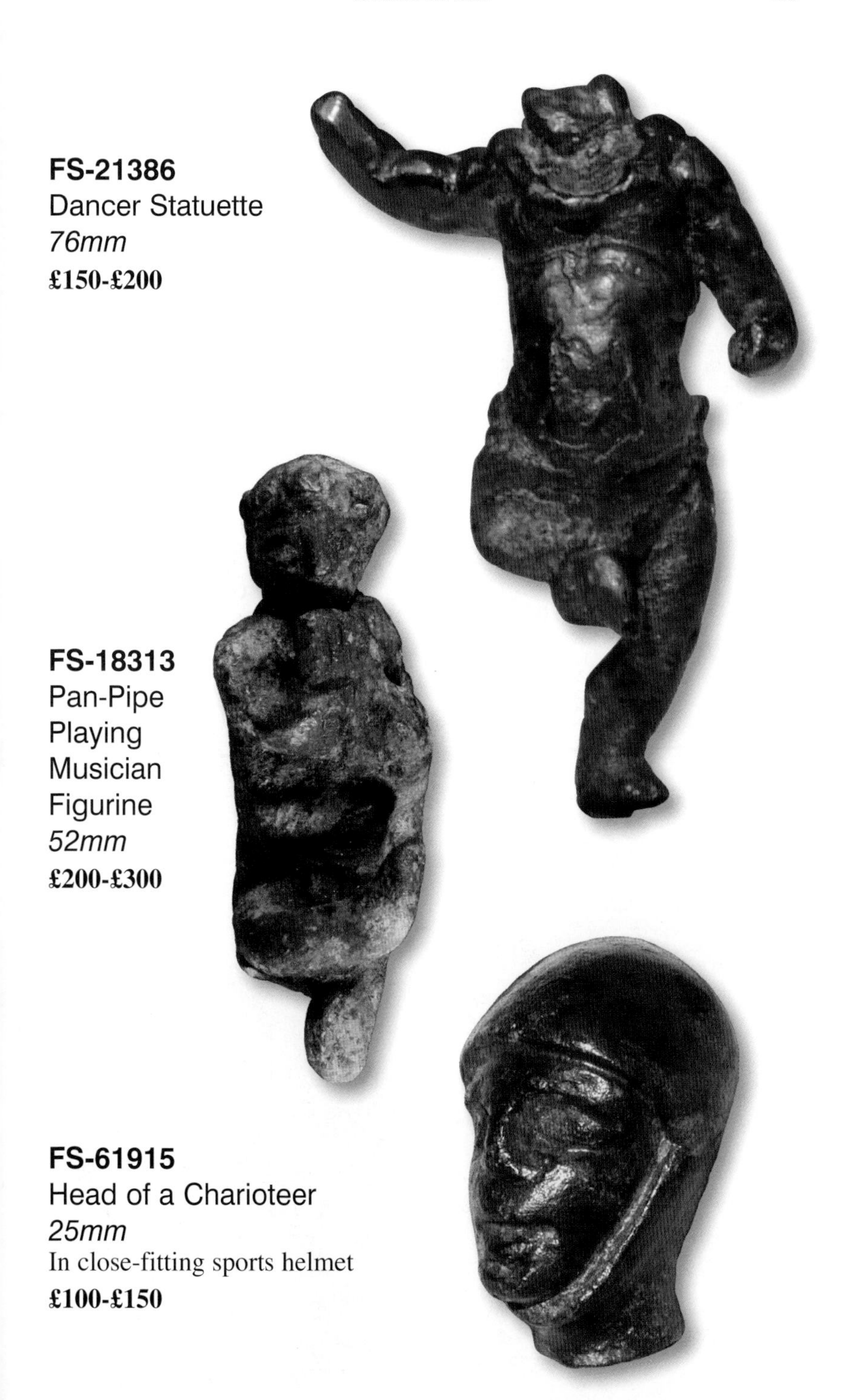

FS-21386
Dancer Statuette
76mm
£150-£200

FS-18313
Pan-Pipe
Playing
Musician
Figurine
52mm
£200-£300

FS-61915
Head of a Charioteer
25mm
In close-fitting sports helmet
£100-£150

FS-16819
Rider Figurine
66mm
For use with a horse model
£100-£150

FS-5820
Male Statuette
225mm
In floor-length robe with arms raised
£1,500-£2,000

FS-51113
Statuette of Caesar Augustus
145mm
Standing with cloak over his head in guise of a priest
£2,000-£3,000

FS-28752
Alexander the Great Figurine
95mm
Copied from the Greek original by Lysippos
£200-£300

FS-3305
Male Torso
78mm
With loose garment to the hips
£800-£1,000

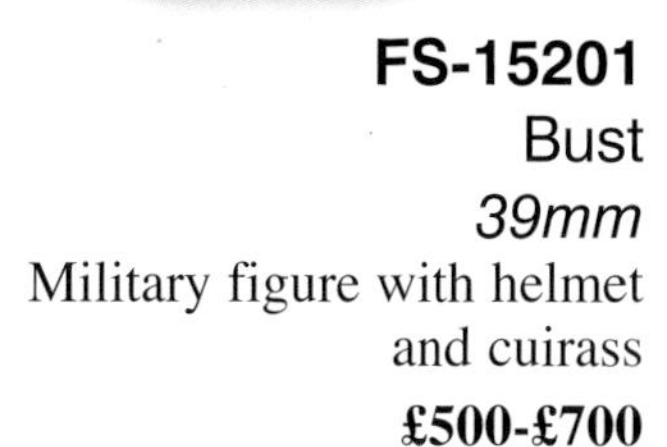

FS-15201
Bust
39mm
Military figure with helmet and cuirass
£500-£700

FS-64738
Bust of a Greek Youth
85mm
With dressed hair
From £1,000

FS-9845
Hero Figurine
69mm
With mantle to the shoulder
£200-£300

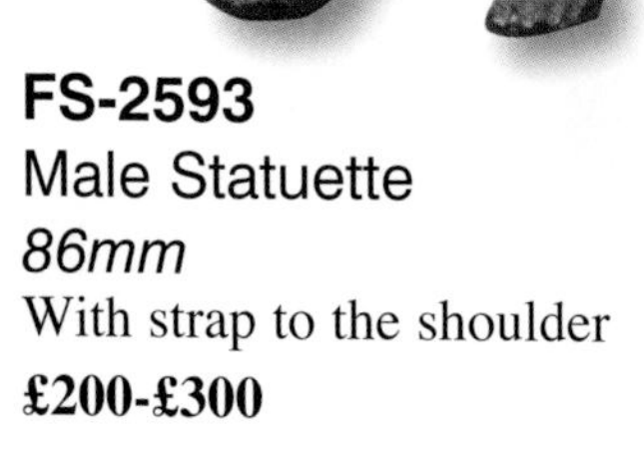

FS-2593
Male Statuette
86mm
With strap to the shoulder
£200-£300

FS-8667
Figurine Head
67mm
With thick hair and beard
£200-£300

FS-16186
Hero Statuette on Base
90mm
Sitting with arms at the sides
£100-£150

FS-18465
Cloaked Male Statuette
67mm
£80-£100

FS-811
Venus Aphrodite Figurine
270mm
Standing nude on socle base
From £40,000

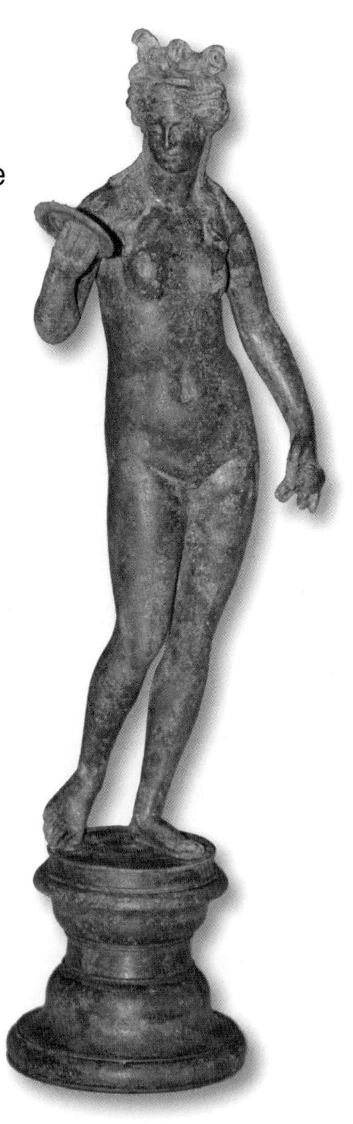

FS-20495
Venus Statuette
120mm
Standing nude with clothing folded to the hips
From £5,000

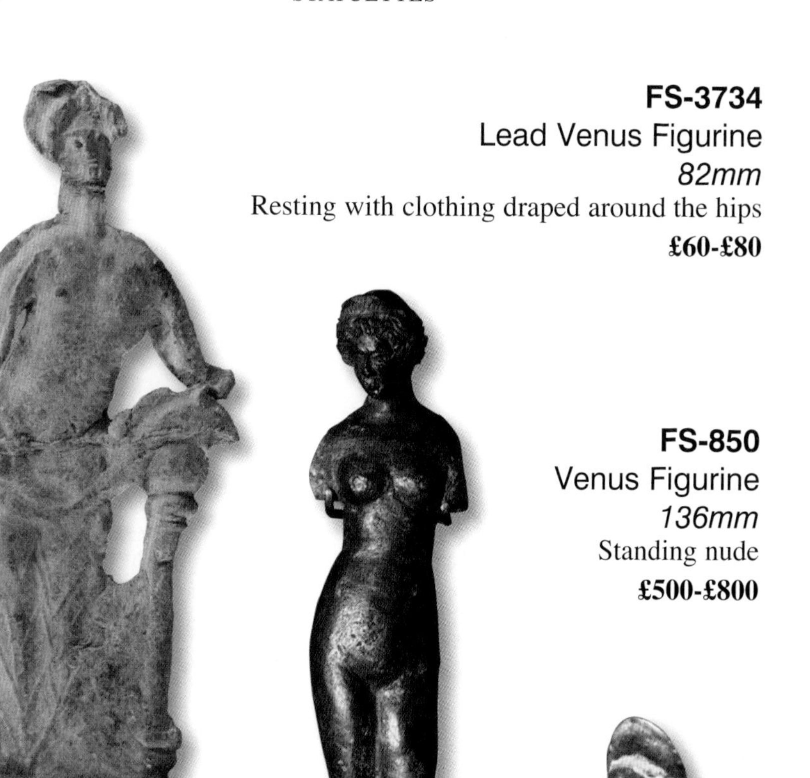

FS-3734
Lead Venus Figurine
82mm
Resting with clothing draped around the hips
£60-£80

FS-850
Venus Figurine
136mm
Standing nude
£500-£800

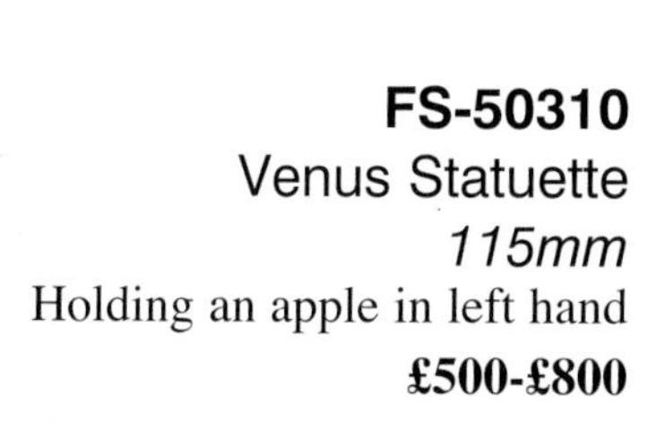

FS-50310
Venus Statuette
115mm
Holding an apple in left hand
£500-£800

FS-6409
Athena Bust Miniature
33mm
With Corinthian helmet
£400-£600

FS-57636
Silver
Athena
Statuette
30mm
Helmeted head
£300-£400

FS-18194
Minerva Bust
76mm
With Corinthian helmet
£400-£600

FS-64735
Bust of Minerva
110mm
With crested helmet
£500-£700

FS-65258
Bust of Minerva
85mm
With crested helmet
£300-£400

FS-7291
Minerva Statuette
84mm
With helmet and loose robe
£300-£400

FS-7856
Minerva Statuette
84mm
With helmet and loose robe
£300-£400

FS-65252
Minerva Statuette
73mm
With helmet and patera
£300-£400

FS-19240
Minerva Figurine
80mm
With helmet and robe
£250-£350

FS-11944
Bust of Minerva
52mm
With helmet and draped robe
£200-£300

FS-45093
Head of Minerva
51mm
In Corinthian helmet
£200-£300

FS-56429
Head of Minerva
57mm
With Corinthian helmet
£200-£300

FS-18202
Minerva
Statuette
54mm
In helmet
and loose
robe
£60-£80

FS-35335
Minerva Statuette
56mm
In loosely draped robe and armour
£100-£150

FS-2543
Diana Figurine
166mm
In tight-fitting clothing
£1,000-£1,500

FS-51758
Diana Statuette
81mm
In tight-fitting clothing drawing an arrow from her quiver
£300-£400

FS-18196
Diana Statuette
61mm
In tight-fitting clothing drawing an arrow to shoot
£200-£300

FS-18195
Concordia Figurine
105mm
With cornucopia
£400-£600

FS-5369
Concordia
Seated Figurine
64mm
With cornucopia
£400-£600

FS-18705
Silver
Concordia
Statuette
36mm
With
cornucopia
and crown
£300-£400

FS-61895
Fortuna Statuette
75mm
With cornucopia and horned
crown
£300-£400

FS-3459
Gold Fortuna Statuette
29mm
With cornucopia and crescent crown
From £2,000

FS-45084
Goddess Fortuna Statuette
33mm
With ship's rudder and distaff
£150-£200

FS-14875
Isis Fortuna Statuette
76mm
With cornucopia and feather crown
£200-£300

FS-6383
Fortuna Statuette
81mm
With ship's rudder and distaff
£250-£350

FS-22801
Fortuna Figurine
77mm
With ship's rudder and distaff
£200-£300

FS-18203
Fortuna Statuette
67mm
With loose robe
£100-£150

FS-8672
Ceres Figurine
78mm
With sheaf of corn
£100-£150

FS-39018
Goddess Tyche Statuette
73mm
Crowned and seated
£100-£150

FS-15233
Demeter Head
70mm
Bust of Demeter on a tapering stem
£200-£300

FS-800
Winged Victory Bust
53mm
Victory with cuirass and helmet
£300-£400

FS-47138

Psyche Balsamarium

260mm

Hinged at the top of the head, silver-inlaid eyes

From £10,000

FS-65008

Luna on Globe Statuette

220mm

Goddess Luna advancing on a globe in loose fitting robe

From £10,000

FS-10395
Bust of a Matron
125mm
With dressed hair and garments
From £1,000

FS-24122
Head of a Matrona
32mm
With dressed hair
£100-£150

FS-64737
Head of Medusa
90mm
With wings to the brow
£800-£1,000

FS-4082
Sheet Gold Statuette
84mm
Female goddess in loose robe
From £8,000

FS-64736
Head of
Medusa
50mm
With snakes tied below
chin in Hercules knot
£600-£800

FS-5548
Female Bust
65mm
With dressed hair
£400-£600

FS-3754
Female Figurine
30mm
With left arm raised, on stand
£100-£150

FS-18707
Goddess Figurine
32mm
£100-£150

FS-10993
Sappho Figurine
88mm
With loosely draped robe, harp on the left arm
£100-£150

FS-38184
Head of a Young Woman
52mm
With dressed hair
£150-£200

FS-26362
Head of a Lady
28mm
With dressed hair
£150-£200

FS-19599
Female Bust
24mm
With dressed hair and mantle
£100-£150

FS-42237
Female Statue Face
36mm
£40-£60

FS-4638
Female
Bust
39mm
With silver
eyes
£80-£100

FS-45072
Model Cornucopia Pair
54mm
Two horns with fruit and other foods flowing from them
£200-£300

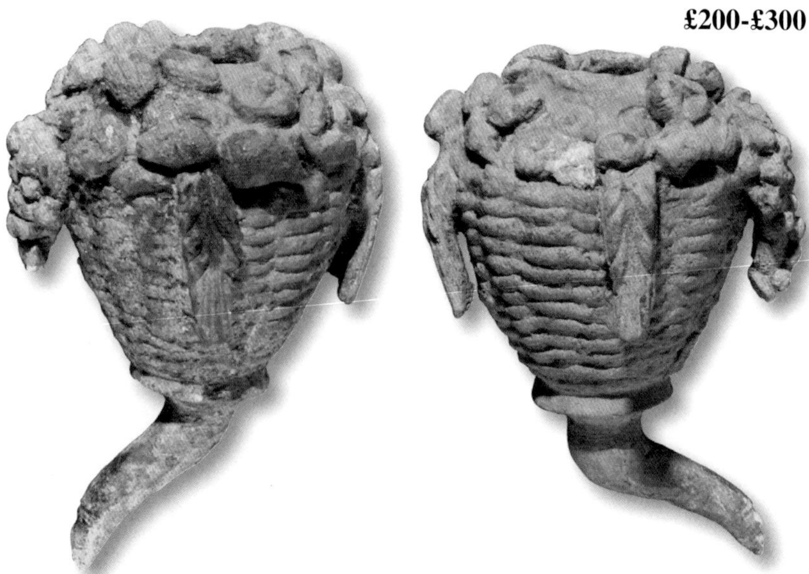

FS-37526

Silver Anthropomorphic Dice Pair

28mm

Dice formed as two sitting nude figures with spots indicating the numbers

From £1,000

FS-54714

Erotic Gaming Piece

32mm

Sitting nude

£100-£150

FS-17759

Silver Votive Club of Hercules

29mm

Club with trimmed branches

£70-£90

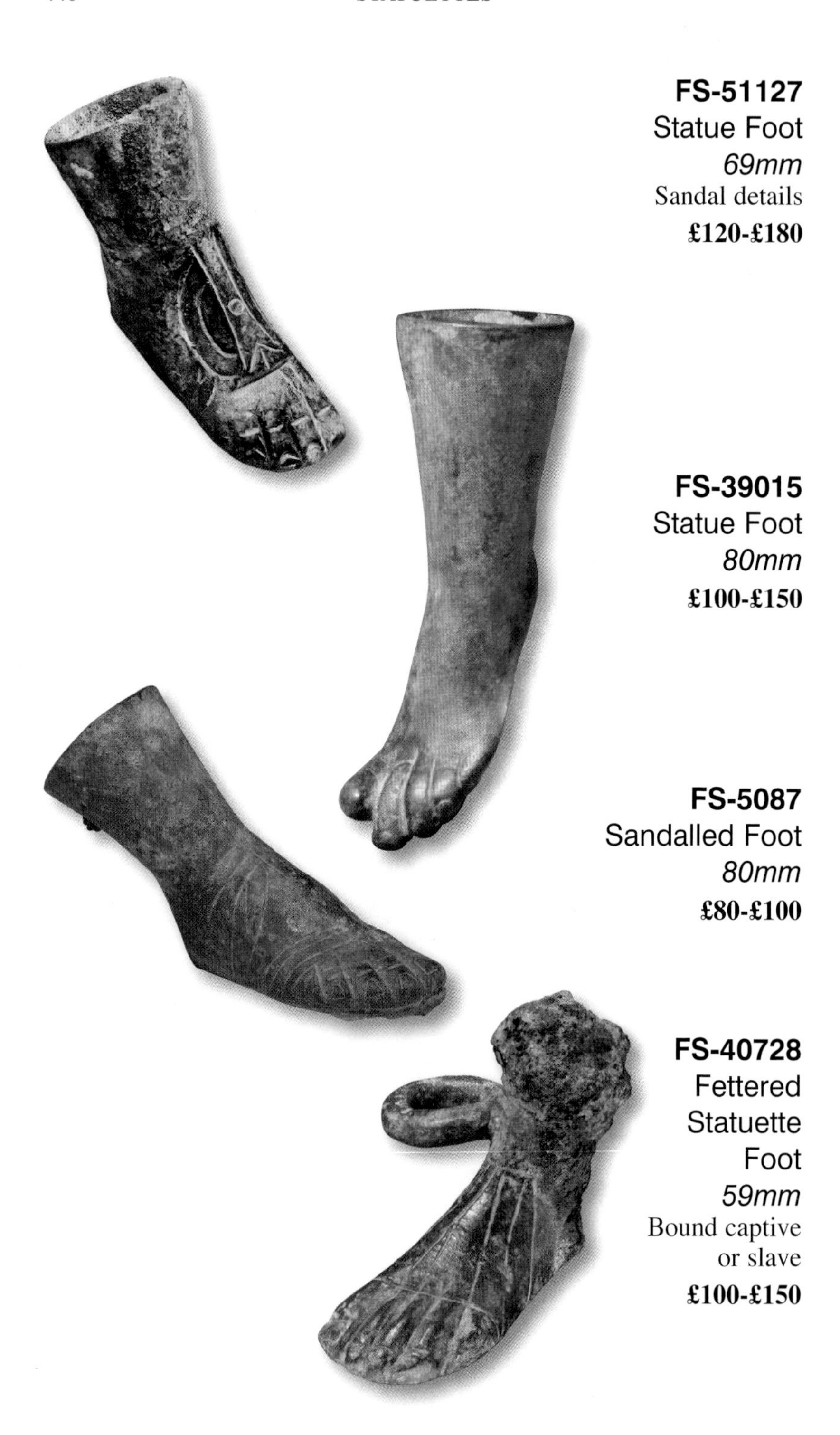

FS-51127
Statue Foot
69mm
Sandal details
£120-£180

FS-39015
Statue Foot
80mm
£100-£150

FS-5087
Sandalled Foot
80mm
£80-£100

FS-40728
Fettered
Statuette
Foot
59mm
Bound captive
or slave
£100-£150

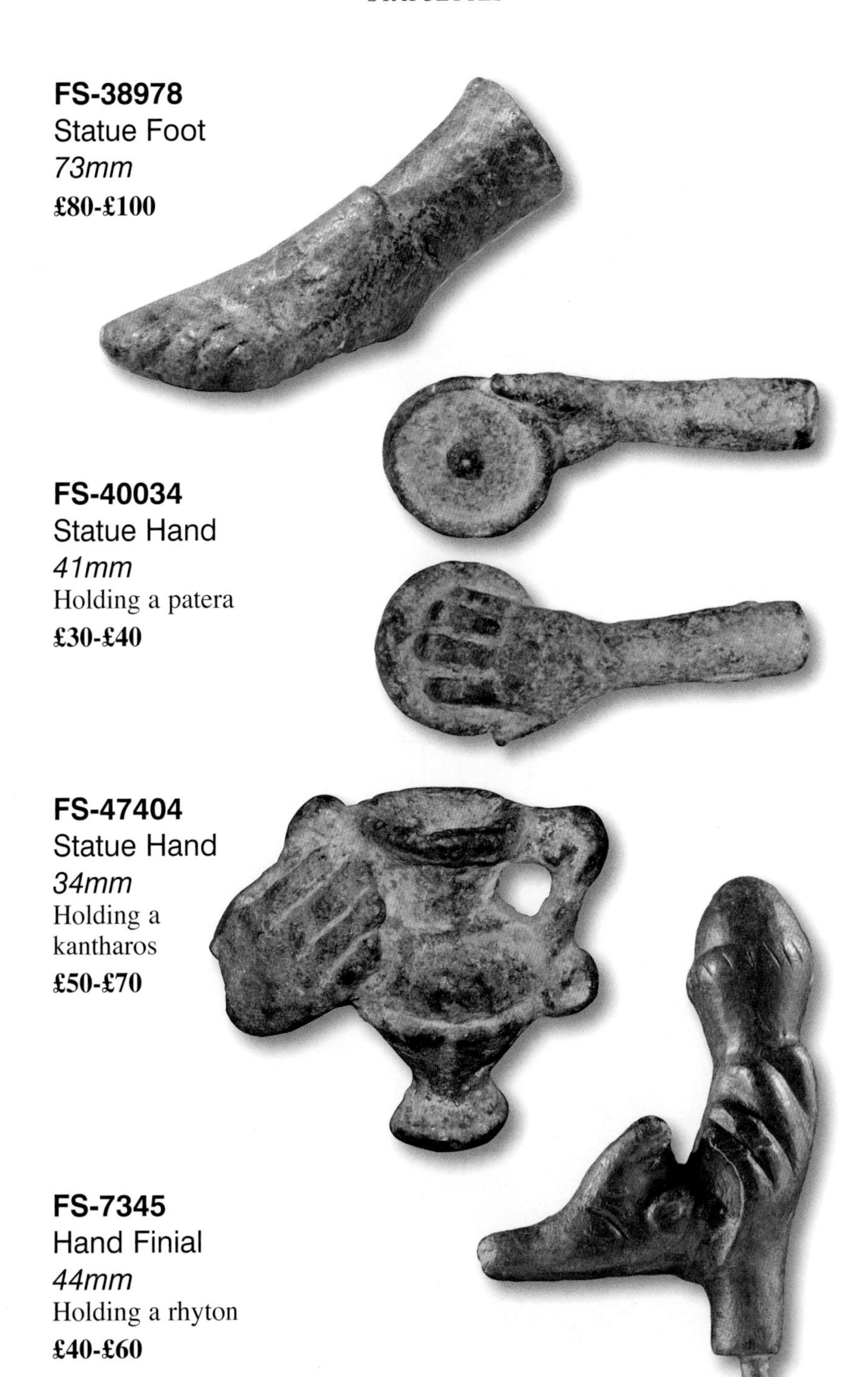

FS-38978
Statue Foot
73mm
£80-£100

FS-40034
Statue Hand
41mm
Holding a patera
£30-£40

FS-47404
Statue Hand
34mm
Holding a kantharos
£50-£70

FS-7345
Hand Finial
44mm
Holding a rhyton
£40-£60

AS-12658
Monumental
Fountain
Lion Figurine
250mm
Spout in the
open mouth
From £2,000

AS-64706
Lion Statuette
76mm
Resting with
forelegs extended
£200-£300

AS-1105
Silver
Lioness
Figurine
42mm
One foreleg
raised
£600-£800

AS-4737
Lioness Figurine
35mm
Resting on a
rectangular base
£150-£200

AS-65766
Lion Statuette
51mm
On rectangular base
£200-£300

AS-28756
Lion Statuette
74mm
With extended forepaws
£80-£100

AS-3356
Lion Mask
32mm
With open mouth
£60-£80

AS-24094
Panther Statuette
46mm
Regardant on a rectangular base
£400-£600

AS-57769
Panther
Statuette
125mm
Pawing the
ground
£200-£300

AS-6558
Panther
Figurine
57mm
One foreleg
raised
£200-£300

AS-57525
Panther
Figurine
30mm
Head turned back
£150-£200

AS-51768
Panther Statuette
45mm
Resting with forelegs extended
£100-£150

AS-24002
Silver Panther Figurine
27mm
In advancing pose
£100-£150

AS-57626
Panther Head
70mm
£150-£200

AS-51763
Panther Head
30mm
£100-£150

AS-5373
Capricorn Figurine
92mm
£500-£700

AS-9769
Bear Statuette
85mm
In advancing pose
£200-£300

AS-2228
Leokampos Figurine
65mm
£400-£600

AS-42163
Dog Statuette
49mm
Standing with tail erect
£100-£150

AS-7411
Dog Figure
44mm
Standing, modelled in the round, fur detail
£100-£150

AS-14754
Hunting Dog's Head Terminal
85mm
£40-£60

AS-2355
Cockerel Figurine
57mm
Standing figure on domed base
£80-£100

AS-22600
Silver Cockerel Figurine
19mm
Standing figure
£100-£150

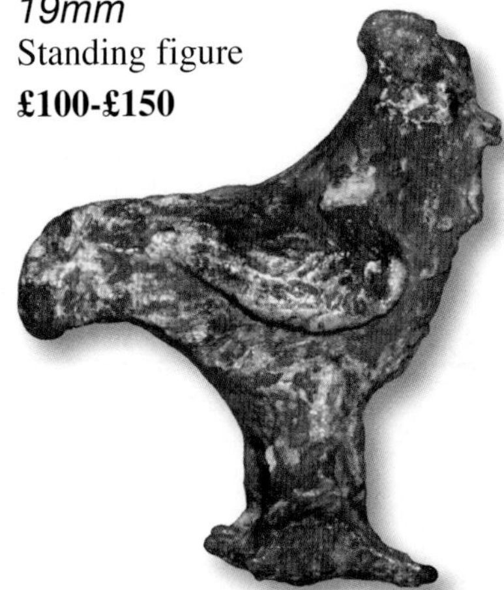

AS-18262
Cockerel Statuette
51mm
Standing figure modelled in the round
£60-£80

AS-8089
Cockerel Figure
32mm
Standing figure on domed base
£50-£70

AS-18841
Aquila Figurine
53mm
Military eagle with ring-and-dot motifs
£100-£150

AS-4385
Silver Eagle Statuette
32mm
Eagle on a rock
£120-£180

AS-35327
Silver Eagle Statuette
18mm
Standing eagle with base
£100-£150

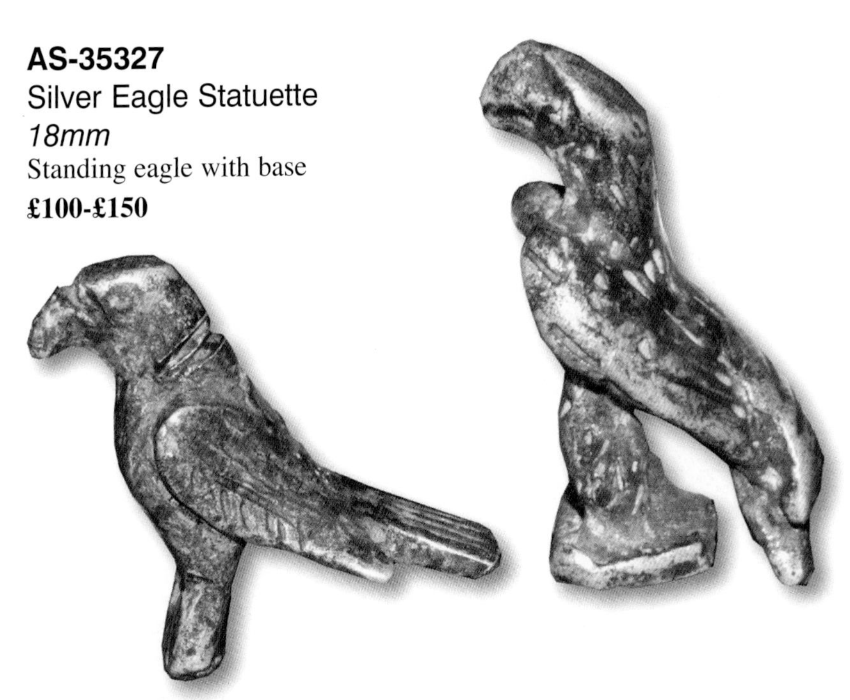

AS-35328
Silver Eagle Statuette
22mm
Standing eagle with peg feet
£100-£150

AS-22907
Silver Eagle Pair
42-44mm
Two standing eagles
From £1,500

AS-35326

Silver Eagle Statuette

18mm

Standing eagle with base

£100-£150

AS-35319

Eagle Statuette

110mm

Standing eagle with rectangle base

£200-£300

AS-111

Eagle with Wreath

58mm

On rectangular base with splayed feet

£150-£200

AS-31451
Eagle Statuette
76mm
On pyramid base
£150-£200

AS-18258
Eagle Statuette
77mm
On pyramid base
£100-£150

AS-46114
Eagle Statuette
58mm
On discoid base
£100-£150

AS-34550
Eagle Statuette
43mm
Modelled in the round
£100-£150

AS-22865
Eagle
Statuette
43mm
£100-£150

AS-23460
Eagle Statuette
48mm
With wings spread
£100-£150

AS-31459
Eagle Statuette
27mm
On socle base
£100-£150

AS-18708
Eagle Statuette
18mm
With flange base
£100-£150

AS-2518
Eagle Statuette
45mm
Modelled in the round
£80-£100

AS-18208
Eagle on Ox-Head Statuette
53mm
On rectangular base
£100-£150

AS-26352
Eagle
Statuette
66mm
On discoid
base, erect
£100-£150

AS-32919
Eagle Figurine
43mm
Modelled in the round
£100-£150

AS-18259
Eagle on Globe Statuette
57mm
On socle base
£100-£150

AS-18209
Eagle Statuette
36mm
On discoid base
£80-£100

AS-18207
Eagle Statuette
46mm
On tiered base
£80-£100

AS-18210
Eagle on Bull Statuette
47mm
Modelled in the round
£100-£150

AS-18264
Eagle on Ox-Head Statuette
27mm
Modelled in the round
£80-£100

AS-28755
Eagle Figurine
60mm
Perched on branch
£80-£100

AS-23415
Bull Statuette
26mm
Modelled in the round
£300-£400

AS-31453
Bull on Base
59mm
On tiered pedestal base
£150-£200

AS-39014
Apis Bull Statuette
73mm
On tiered base
£200-£300

AS-21665
Bull Statuette
55mm
Modelled in the round
£120-£180

AS-21331
Bull Statuette
44mm
Modelled in the round
£100-£150

AS-23213
Bull Statuette
52mm
£100-£150

AS-18268
Bull Statuette
44mm
On tiered base
£80-£100

AS-21325
Bull Statuette
44mm
With head raised
£80-£100

AS-18260
Bull Figurine
54mm
On socle base
£100-£150

AS-11567
Leaping
Stallion
Figurine
53mm
With forelegs
extended
£300-£400

AS-31450
Prancing Horse
Statuette
67mm
One foreleg
extended
£150-£200

AS-61609
Ram Statuette
46mm
Modelled in the round
£100-£150

AS-60762
Ram Statuette
40mm
With fur texture
£200-£300

AS-57629
Ram Statuette
55mm
With fur detailing
£200-£300

AS-28010
Ram Statuette
68mm
With legs folded beneath the body
£200-£300

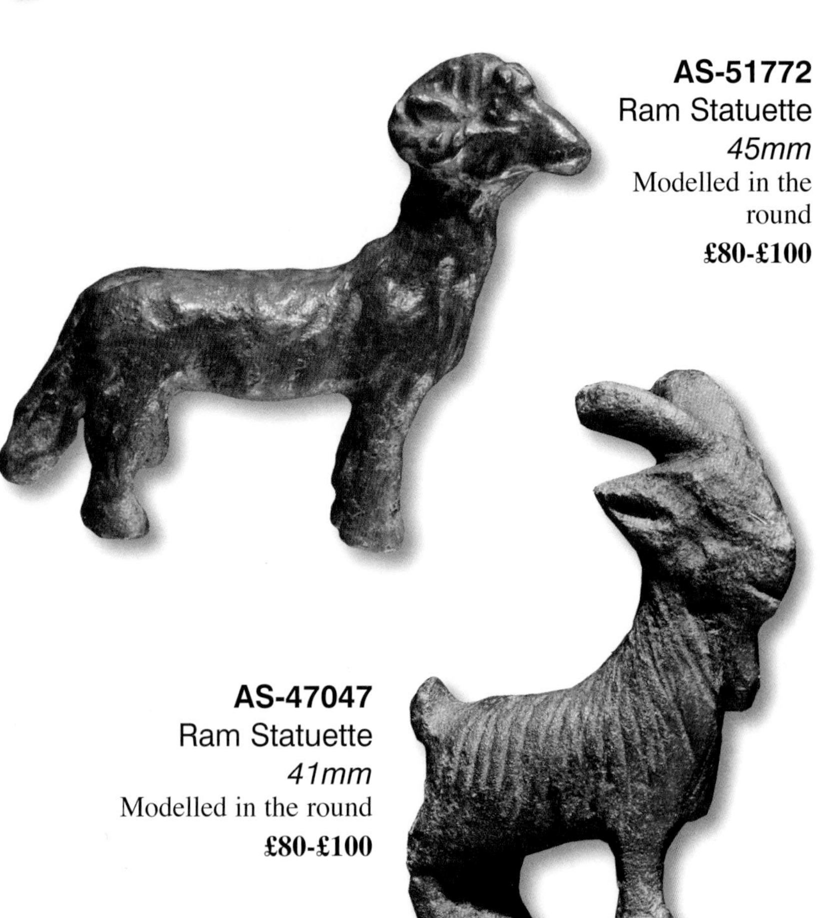

AS-51772
Ram Statuette
45mm
Modelled in the round
£80-£100

AS-47047
Ram Statuette
41mm
Modelled in the round
£80-£100

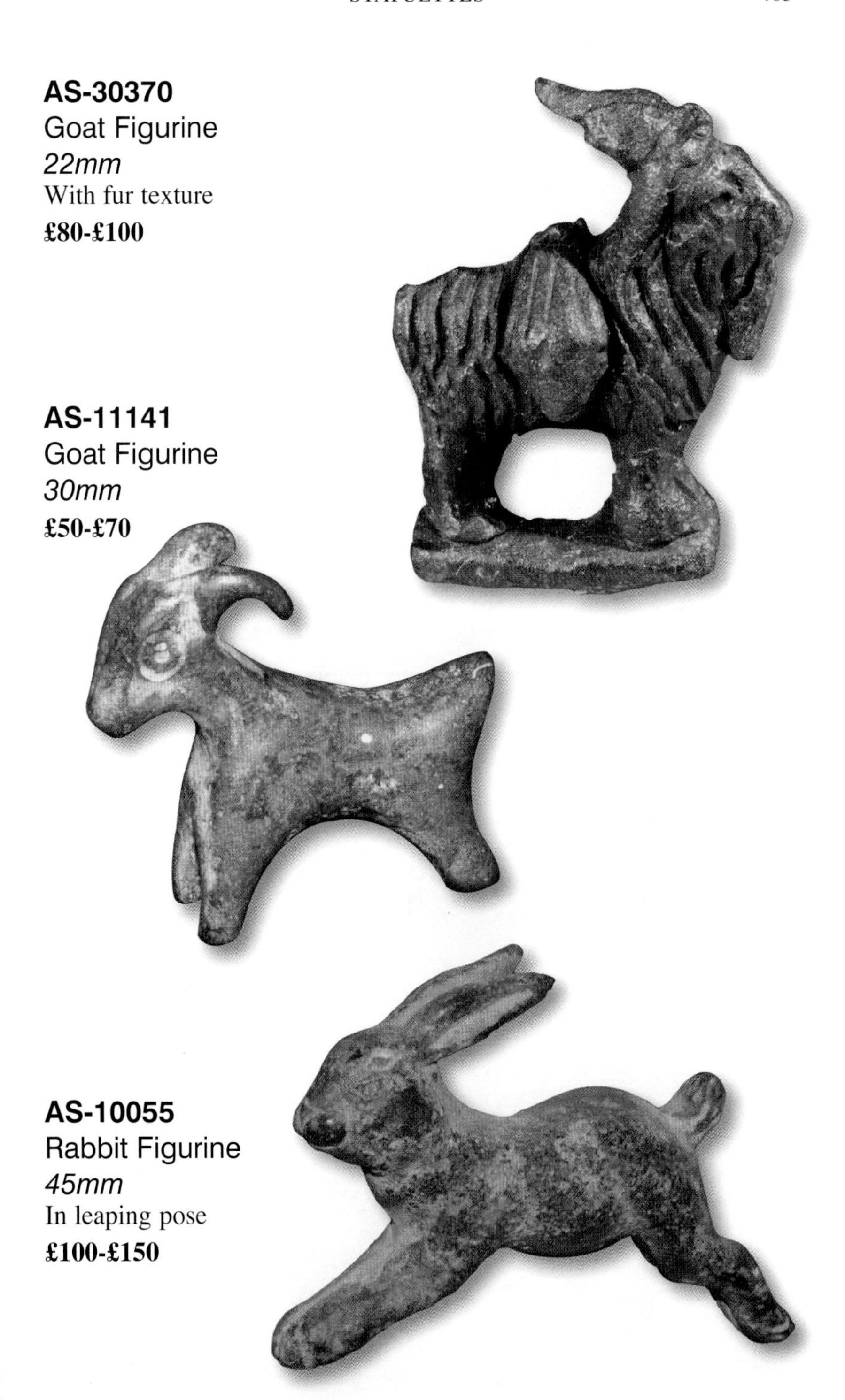

AS-30370
Goat Figurine
22mm
With fur texture
£80-£100

AS-11141
Goat Figurine
30mm
£50-£70

AS-10055
Rabbit Figurine
45mm
In leaping pose
£100-£150

AS-34508
Silver Mouse with Nut Figurine
30mm
Modelled in the round
£200-£300

AS-2690
Silver Sow Figurine
21mm
Modelled in the round
£300-£400

AS-20048
Pig Statuette
55mm
With head raised
£120-£180

AS-25602
Boar Statuette
55mm
Modelled in the round
£120-£180

AS-23212
Boar Statuette
54mm
With prominent bristle crest
£120-£180

AS-18839
Boar Statuette
50mm
With head lowered
£120-£180

AS-16816
Boar
Figurine
55mm
Modelled in
the round
£120-£180

AS-33953
Votive Boar
Figurine
29mm
Flat-section
plaque
£100-£150